# Classification of the Animal Kingdom

# CLASSIFICATION

## OF THE

# ANIMAL KINGDOM

Richard E. Blackwelder

SOUTHERN ILLINOIS UNIVERSITY PRESS     *Carbondale, Illinois*

# CONTENTS

69758

INTRODUCTION                                                              1

Simplified List of Recent Phyla                                          6

Simplified List of Recent Classes and Orders,
   with Common Names                                       9

Notes on the Taxa                                                       26

Complete List of Phyla                                                  36

Complete List of Classes and Orders,
   with Synonyms, Subgroups, and Geologic Range           39

BIBLIOGRAPHY                                                            72

INDEX TO COMMON NAMES                                                   75

INDEX TO LATIN NAMES                                                    80

# INTRODUCTION

THE CLASSIFICATION OF ANIMALS is still very much a field in which discovery and revision are continuing, even after two hundred years of study. The importance of classification in biology increases every year, because the experimental and practical fields find increasing need for accurate identification of animals and for understanding of comparative relationships.

At least one outstanding biologist has opposed publication of this new classification on the ground that it would be accepted as final, *the* classification, and would tend to make students think that all higher classification is finished. The intention of the compiler is just the opposite. Just as this classification is different in detail from all previous ones, so will future editions be still different, as we learn more about the comparative features of animals.

It is anticipated that every new edition will spur students of the individual groups to propose improvements. It is therefore planned to issue corrected editions whenever appropriate. The very appearance of these subsequent editions will emphasize the growth of understanding of animal groups.

Only one ostensibly complete classification of animals, living and fossil, has been published in recent years. That classification, by A. S. Pearse of Duke University, is a good one, based on the views of many specialists. Certain mechanical faults make it less usable than it should be, and the need for revision gave the original impetus to preparation of the present classification. Because Pearse did not usually indicate the source of his arrangements, he is not here cited as an authority. Nevertheless, the two classifications are basically very similar. No other single classification has been found that agrees so closely with the conclusions of the present study.

It should be emphasized that, within certain limits, this classification is not a simple compilation of the views of specific workers. In nearly all details, choices have been made between conflicting schemes of various authors, not on the basis of the reputation of those authors but on my judgment of the soundness of their supporting arguments or on my analysis of the data they present. In none of the larger groups has the work of any single author been accepted without modification.

Several considerations have influenced the decisions embodied in this classification.

*First,* a false picture is given by a simplified classification, because the existing diversity is one of the principal features of the animal kingdom. Therefore, no groups should be combined merely for the sake of simplicity.

*Second,* although the previous item would seem to require coverage of the groupings at all possible levels, to show the extreme range of division and subdivision, this is not in fact possible. Not only are there many conflicting groupings at certain levels, such as of phyla or orders, but there is no practical way to show these groupings in a general classification. It is a compromise that is believed to be effective to subdivide the phyla only into classes, subclasses, and orders. Other possible groupings, such as subphyla and superorders are referred to in the notes.

*Third,* two groups which are so distinct at any level that they cannot be described in common terms must be separated at that level. (For example, Pterobranchia and Enteropneusta; see the Notes on the Taxa.)

*Fourth,* groups which cannot be distinguished at any particular level by the type of characters used for their neighbors must be combined at that level. (For example, the sometime classes of Nematoda.)

*Fifth,* the discovery of groupings within a class, for example, does not justify the creation of new classes for each of the subgroups. The proper level for the new groups can only be determined by comparison with neighboring parts of the classification.

*Sixth,* although uniformity in the form (endings) of names at each level would unquestionably be helpful, it cannot now be attained without adding greatly to the total of name forms and synonyms. The systems so far proposed are so diverse as to introduce further confusion of their own. None of the systems has been widely enough accepted to be entitled to adoption throughout the Animal Kingdom. None has been so widely accepted on a world basis, even in one group, as to indicate universal acceptance in the near future. Indeed, even the ordinal endings in *-iformes* adopted by American ichthyologists and ornithologists are almost entirely unused in the rest of the world. The resulting names are unnecessarily long and cumbersome. The system does not relieve any-one from learning the shorter forms also. The latter are used here, with the uniform-ending forms listed as synonyms. In other groups, usage of the source of the classification is followed as to spelling, in most cases. There are a variety of systems in use and no obvious trend to-ward adoption of any single system.

This classification attempts to show the various spellings as well as the various synonyms. Each zoologist will choose which one he wishes to use in each case.

*Seventh,* no single rule will suffice for choice of names where several apply to a single taxon. Reasons for each decision are given in the text in many cases, but in general it has been the goal to retain the best known names, at the most appropriate level, regardless of homonymy. Priority is considered to be of secondary importance at these levels.

*Eighth,* although considerable homonymy exists at all levels, even up to that of phylum names, there is almost no real confusion caused thereby. Until there are direct rules to govern the decisions, there seems to be nothing gained by replacing well known names, such as Decapoda (either in the Cephalopoda or in the Crustacea).

This classification is in three parts, the purposes of which are quite different. In order of preparation, these are:   1] the complete classifica-tion, including lists of the phyla and of the classes and orders, of all ani-mals, living and fossil;   2] the justification for unusual features in this classification; and   3] a simplified classification of Recent animals for student use, with common names, again including lists of the phyla and of the classes and orders. The arrangement of these parts in the book is just the reverse of this.

In both lists, the phyla are first arranged in four subkingdoms, and one of these is divided into four series. Many other groupings of these phyla are possible, and several are shown in the footnotes of the section Complete List of Phyla. It is not here believed that these supra-phylum groupings are of much significance at this phase of the knowledge of animals.

In both lists of orders, these orders are arranged in the appropri-ate classes and subclasses. No other levels, such as superorder, are recognized. They may be of use in some circumstances but seem to be of little value in showing the arrangement of the orders on a practical basis.

Throughout, rejected synonyms are printed in italics, the accepted class names are in capital letters, and the subclass names and the order names are both set in capitals and lower case letters. In the footnotes, names that also appear in the classification above are printed in small capitals. The other names in the footnotes are somewhat in the nature of rejected synonyms, but as most of them are really the names of non-accepted groupings, they appear in capitals and lower case roman letters.

To the variety of spellings there is no end. No attempt is made to list *all* forms, but such spellings as would appear at a separate place in an alphabetical index are listed, along with those variations that are used for distinct levels; e.g., Echiuroidea (phylum), Echiurida (class), and Echiuroina (order).

In the Complete List of Orders the geologic range of each group is shown by symbols at the right margin. The meaning of these symbols is shown in the following table.

| | | | |
|-----|-----|-----|-----|
| REC | Recent | JUR | Jurassic |
| QUA | Quaternary | MES | Mesozoic |
| PLE | Pleistocene | PER | Permian |
| PLI | Pliocene | PEN | Pennsylvanian |
| OLI | Oligocene | MIS | Mississippian |
| MIO | Miocene | CAR | Carboniferous |
| EOC | Eocene (+ Paleocene) | DEV | Devonian |
| TER | Tertiary | SIL | Silurian |
| CEN | Cenozoic | ORD | Ordovician |
| CRE | Cretaceous | CAM | Cambrian |
| TRI | Triassic | PAL | Paleozoic |

There are a few points of discrepancy between the Simplified List and the Complete List. These are intentional, to make the simplified list more useful to students. The Complete List shows the definitive classification that is here being proposed.

The names included under the footnote heading *"Includes"* may be suborders, synonyms, rejected groups, or names of questionable application. They are all names which have at some time been used for orders or more inclusive groups and are included merely to indicate their approximate position in the scheme.

Several recent schemes of classification in particular groups are known to the compiler but are not followed herein. Some were received too late for study (e.g., part W of the Treatise of Invertebrate Paleontology). Some were not yet available in the form needed for our use and so were not considered (e.g., Echinodermata by H. B. Fell and Mollusca by Taylor and Sohl). There is no judgment of these schemes implied in this action; they will be considered for a subsequent revised edition.

It will probably be thought by some that this is an extreme classification in separating many small groups as distinct phyla. The compiler believes that it is a conservative classification even in this regard. He believes that an important basic tenet of classification, too often overlooked, is that all groups must be distinct and definable and that therefore forms are not to be forced into existing groups at any level if they do not agree with what are deemed to be the important features of that group. The important features in this case are those which caused the group to be set aside and maintained as distinct.

It is sometimes possible to enlarge slightly the scope of a group definition to admit forms previously unknown, but this does not justify including widely divergent forms that cannot be defined together effectively.

# Simplified List

## Kingdom **ANIMALIA**[1]

**EOZOA**
    Protozoa [2]    [one-celled animals] [3]

**PARAZOA**
    Porifera    sponges

**AGNOTOZOA**
    Mesozoa

**HISTOZOA** (*Metazoa*)
    Enterocoela
        Monoblastozoa
        Coelenterata (*Cnidaria*)    hydroids, jellyfish, medusae, corals,
            sea-anemones
        Ctenophora    comb-jellies, sea-walnuts
    Acoelomata
        Platyhelminthes    flatworms
        Rhynchocoela (*Nemertinea*)    ribbon-worms, proboscis-worms
    Pseudocoelomata
        Acanthocephala    spiny-headed-worms
        Rotifera (*Rotatoria*)    rotifers, wheel-animalcules
        Gastrotricha
        Kinorhyncha (*Echinodera*)
        Priapuloidea
        Nematoda    thread-worms, round-worms
        Gordiacea (*Nematomorpha*)    horsehair-worms,
            gordian-worms
        Calyssozoa (*Endoprocta*)

# of Recent Phyla

| Subk | Series | Phylum |
|------|--------|--------|

Coelomata

    Bryozoa (*Ectoprocta*)   moss-animals
    Phoronida
    Brachiopoda   lamp-shells
    Mollusca   mollusks
    Sipunculoidea
    Echiuroidea
    Myzostomida
    Annelida   [segmented worms]
    Tardigrada   bear-animalcules, water-bears
    Pentastomida
    Onychophora
    Arthropoda   crustaceans, arachnids, insects, etc.
    Chaetognatha   arrow-worms
    Pogonophora   beard-worms
    Echinodermata
    Pterobranchia
    Enteropneusta
    Planctosphaeroidea
    Tunicata   sea-squirts
    Cephalochordata   lancelets
    Vertebrata   vertebrates

[1] For explanations, other synonyms, extinct groups, and other taxa above the phylum level, see the section Complete List of Phyla.

[2] The Protozoa are sometimes placed in a separate kingdom of organisms—the Protista.

[3] Non-Latin names can be made for each phylum by merely using the English form of the name, such as protozoans for Protozoa or arthropods for Arthropoda. These are listed only where they are in common use.

# Simplified List of Recent Classes and Orders

## with Common Names

Class    Subcl    Order

### PROTOZOA

FLAGELLATA (*Mastigophora*)   flagellates
    Phytomastigina   [plant-like flagellates]
        Chrysomonadina   silicoflagellates, etc.
        Coccolithophorida   coccolithophores, coccoliths
        Cryptomonadina
        Phytomonadina (*Volvocales*)
        Euglenoidina
        Chloromonadina
        Dinoflagellata   dinoflagellates
    Zoomastigina   [animal-like flagellates]
        Rhizomastigina
        Protomonadina
        Polymastigina
        Hypermastigina
SARCODINA
    Rhizopoda   rhizopods
        Proteomyxa
        Mycetozoa   slime-molds
        Amoebozoa
        Testacea
        Foraminifera   foraminiferans, forams
    Actinopoda
        Heliozoa   sun-animalcules
        Radiolaria   radiolarians
SPOROZOA
    Telosporidia
        Gregarinida
        Coccidia
        Haemosporidia
    Cnidosporidia
        Myxosporidia
        Actinomyxidia

Class    Subcl    Order

          Microsporidia    microsporidians
          Helicosporidia
      Sarcosporidia
          Sarcosporidia
          Globidia
      Haplosporidia
          Haplosporidia
CILIATA    ciliates
      Protociliata
          Opalinida    opalinids
      Euciliata
          Holotricha
          Spirotricha    tintinnids, etc.
          Chonotricha
          Peritricha
SUCTORIA
          Suctoria


# PORIFERA

sponges

CALCAREA (*Calcispongea*)    [calcareous sponges, chalky sponges]
          Solenida
          Lebetida
          Pharetronida
          Thalamida
HYALOSPONGEA (*Hexactinellida*)    glass-sponges
          Lyssakina
          Dictyonina
          Lychniskophora
          Heteractinida
DEMOSPONGEA
          Myxospongida
          Keratosida    horny-sponges
          Haplosclerida
          Poecilosclerida
          Hadromerida
          Halichondrida
          Epipolasida
          Choristida
          Carnosida
          Lithistida    stone-sponges

# MESOZOA

RHOMBOZOA
>Dicyemida
>Heterocyemida

ORTHONECTIDA
>Orthonectida

# MONOBLASTOZOA

MONOBLASTOIDEA
>Monoblastidea

# COELENTERATA
### (*Cnidaria*)

coelenterates, medusae

HYDROZOA
>Trachylinida
>Hydroida
>Milleporida (*Hydrocorallinae*)   millepores
>Stylasterina
>Siphonophora   siphonophores

SCYPHOZOA   jellyfishes
>Stauromedusae
>Cubomedusae
>Coronatae
>Semaeostomeae
>Rhizostomeae

ANTHOZOA   sea-anemones, corals
>Alcyonaria
>>Stolonifera
>>Telestacea
>>Alcyonacea   soft-corals
>>Coenothecalia   blue-corals
>>Gorgonacea   sea-fans, horny-corals, gorgonians, sea-feathers
>>Pennatulacea   sea-pens, sea-pansies
>Zoantharia
>>Zoanthiniaria
>>Corallimorpharia
>>Actiniaria   sea-anemones
>>Scleractinia (*Madreporaria*)   hexacorals, stony-corals

Ceriantipatharia
  Antipatharia   black-corals, thorny-corals
  Ceriantharia

# CTENOPHORA
comb-jellies, sea-walnuts

TENTACULATA
  Cydippida
  Lobata
  Cestida
  Platyctenea
NUDA
  Beroida

# PLATYHELMINTHES
flatworms

TURBELLARIA   planarians
  Acoela
  Rhabdocoela
  Alloeocoela
  Tricladida   triclads
  Polycladida   polyclads
TREMATODA   flukes
  Monogenea
  Aspidogastrea
  Digenea
CESTODA   tapeworms
  Proteocephala
  Tetraphyllidea
  Disculicepitidea
  Lecanicephala
  Trypanorhyncha
  Cyclophyllidea
  Aporidea
  Nippotaeniidea
  Caryophyllidea
  Spathebothridea
  Pseudophyllidea
CESTODARIA
  Amphilinidea
  Gyrocotylidea
  Biporophyllidea

# RHYNCHOCOELA

ribbon-worms, proboscis-worms

NEMERTINEA
        Palaeonemertea
        Heteronemertea
        Hoplonemertea
        Bdellonemertea

# ACANTHOCEPHALA

spiny-headed-worms

ACANTHOCEPHALA
        Archiacanthocephala
        Palaeacanthocephala
        Eoacanthocephala

# ROTIFERA
(*Rotatoria*)

rotifers, wheel-animalcules

SEISONIDEA
        Seisonacea
BDELLOIDEA
        Bdellacea
MONOGONONTA
        Ploima
        Flosculariacea
        Collothecacea

# GASTROTRICHA

gastrotrichs

MACRODASYOIDEA
        Macrodasyidea
CHAETONOTOIDEA
        Chaetonotidea

# KINORHYNCHA

ECHINODERA
        Echinodera

# PRIAPULOIDEA

PRIAPULOIDEA
>Priapulida

# NEMATODA

nematodes, nemas, thread-worms, round-worms

NEMATOIDEA
>Enoploidea
>Dorylaimoidea
>Mermithoidea
>Chromadoroidea
>Araeolaimoidea
>Monhysteroidea
>Desmoscolecoidea
>Rhabditoidea
>Rhabdiasoidea
>Oxyuroidea
>Ascaroidea
>Strongyloidea
>Spiruroidea
>Dracunculoidea
>Filarioidea
>Trichuroidea
>Dioctophymoidea

# GORDIACEA

gordian-worms, horsehair-worms

NEMATOMORPHA
>Gordioidea
>Nectonematoidea

# CALYSSOZOA

endoprocts

ENDOPROCTA  (*Entoprocta*)

>Pedicellinida

# BRYOZOA

sea-mats, corallines, moss-animals, bryozoans, sea-mosses

PHYLACTOLAEMATA
Lophopoda
GYMNOLAEMATA
Cyclostomata
Ctenostomata
Cheilostomata

# PHORONIDA

phoronids

PHORONIDA
Phoronida

# BRACHIOPODA

lamp-shells, brachiopods

INARTICULATA
Atremata
Neotremata
ARTICULATA
Protremata
Telotremata

# MOLLUSCA

mollusks

MONOPLACOPHORA
Tryblidioidea
AMPHINEURA    chitons
Neoloricata
APLACOPHORA (*Solenogastres*)
Neomeniida
Chaetodermatida
GASTROPODA    snails, slugs, gastropods
Prosobranchia
Archaeogastropoda    limpets, ear-shells, turbans
Caenogastropoda
Opisthobranchia
Pleurocoela    sea-hares

Class    Subcl    Order

            Pteropoda   butterfly-shells, pteropods
            Sacoglossa
            Acoela   nudibranchs
      Pulmonata   land-snails, slugs
            Basommatophora   boat-shells, ramshorns
            Stylommatophora   slugs
BIVALVIA (*Pelecypoda, Lamellibranchiata*)   bivalves, oysters, clams,
                mussels, pelecypods
            Protobranchia
            Filibranchia
            Eulamellibranchia
            Septibranchia
SCAPHOPODA   tooth-shells, tusk-shells
            Scaphopoda
CEPHALOPODA   cephalopods
      Tetrabranchiata
            Nautiloidea   pearly-nautilus
      Dibranchiata
            Decapoda   squids, cuttle-fish
            Octopoda   octopuses, argonauts
            Vampyromorpha

## SIPUNCULOIDEA

[sipunculid worms]

SIPUNCULOIDEA
            Sipunculida

## ECHIUROIDEA

ECHIURIDA
            Echiuroina
            Xenopneusta
            Heteromyota
SACCOSOMATIDA
            Saccosomatida

## MYZOSTOMIDA

MYZOSTOMIDA
            Proboscidea
            Pharyngidea

## ANNELIDA

[segmented worms] annelids

Class    Subcl    Order
CHAETOPODA
    Polychaeta    polychaetes
        Errantia    sandworms
        Sedentaria    tubeworms
    Oligochaeta    earthworms, angle-worms, night-crawlers, oligochaetes
        Plesiothecata
        Prosothecata
        Prosopora
        Opisthopora
HIRUDINEA    leeches, bloodsuckers
        Rhynchobdellida
        Gnathobdellida
        Pharyngobdellida
        Acanthobdellida
ARCHIANNELIDA
        Archiannelida

## TARDIGRADA

bear-animalcules, water-bears

HETEROTARDIGRADA
        Arthrotardigrada
        Echiniscoidea
EUTARDIGRADA
        Eutardigrada

## PENTASTOMIDA

LINGUATULIDA
        Cephalobaenida
        Porocephalida

## ONYCHOPHORA

PERIPATIDEA
        Euonychophora

## ARTHROPODA

arthropods

MEROSTOMATA
    Xiphosura
        Xiphosurida    horseshoe-crabs
PYCNOGONIDA    sea-spiders
        Eupantopoda

Class    Subcl    Order

ARACHNIDA    arachnids

    Latigastra

        Scorpionida    scorpions

        Pseudoscorpionida    book-scorpions, false-scorpions, pseudoscorpions

        Phalangida (*Opiliones*)    harvest-men, Daddy-long-legs

        Acarida    mites, ticks, chiggers

    Caulogastra

        Palpigradida    microscorpions

        Thelyphonida    whip-scorpions

        Schizomida

        Phrynichida    tailless-whip-scorpions

        Araneida (*Araneae*)    spiders, tarantulas, black-widows

        Solpugida (*Solifugae*)    solpugids, sun-spiders

        Ricinuleida (*Podogonata*)

CRUSTACEA    crustaceans

    Branchiopoda

        Anostraca    brine-shrimps

        Notostraca    phyllopods, fairy-shrimps

        Conchostraca

        Cladocera    water-fleas

    Cephalocarida

        Cephalocarida

    Ostracoda

        Myodocopida

        Podocopida

    Mystacocarida

        Mystacocarida

    Copepoda (*Eucopepoda*)

        Calanoida

        Harpacticoida

        Cyclopoida

        Notodelphyoida

        Monstrilloida

        Caligoida

        Lernaeopodoida

    Branchiura

        Branchiura

    Cirripedia    barnacles

        Thoracica

        Acrothoracica

Ascothoracica
Apoda
Rhizocephala
Malacostraca
Nebaliacea
Anaspidacea
Mysidacea   opossum-shrimps
Thermosbaenacea
Spelaeogriphacea
Lophogastridea
Cumacea
Tanaidacea
Isopoda   pillbugs, sowbugs
Amphipoda   scuds
Euphausiacea   krill
Decapoda   crabs, lobsters, crayfish, shrimps, prawns
Stomatopoda   mantis-shrimps
PAUROPODA
Heterognatha
SYMPHYLA
Cephalostigmata
DIPLOPODA   millipedes
Pselaphognatha
Ancyrotricha
Lophotricha
Chilognatha
Limacomorpha
Oniscomorpha
Ascospermophora
Colobognatha
Nematophora
Proterospermophora
Opisthospermophora
CHILOPODA   centipedes
Pleurostigmophora
Geophilomorpha
Scolopendromorpha
Lithobiomorpha
Craterostigma
Notostigmophora
Scutigeromorpha

Class    Subcl    Order

INSECTA (*Hexapoda*)    insects
    Apterygota
        Protura    proturans
        Thysanura    silver-fish, bristle-tails, rock-jumpers
        Entotrophi    campodeids, japygids
        Collembola    springtails, snow-fleas
    Exopterygota (*Heterometabola*)
        Ephemerida    mayflies
        Odonata    dragonflies, damselflies, mosquito-hawks, devil's-darning-needles, snake-doctors
        Plecoptera    stone-flies, salmonflies
        Grylloblattoidea    grylloblattids
        Orthoptera (*Saltatoria*)    grasshoppers, crickets, locusts, katydids, mole-crickets
        Phasmidia    walking-sticks, stick-insects, leaf-insects
        Blattaria    roaches, cockroaches, croton-bugs
        Mantodea    praying-mantis, soothsayers, mantids
        Dermaptera    earwigs
        Embioptera    embiids, webspinners
        Isoptera    termites, white-ants
        Psocoptera (*Corrodentia*)    psocids, book-lice, bark-lice, dust-lice
        Zoraptera    zorapterans
        Mallophaga    bird-lice, biting-lice
        Thysanoptera    thrips
        Homoptera    cicadas, leaf-hoppers, tree-hoppers, aphids, scale-insects, spittle-bugs, mealy-bugs, frog-spit, psyllids, lantern-flies, white-flies
        Heteroptera    bugs, bed-bugs
        Anoplura    sucking-lice, lice
    Endopterygota (*Holometabola*)
        Neuroptera    snake-flies, serpent-flies, lace-wings, ant-lions, dobson-flies, fish-flies, orl-flies
        Mecoptera    scorpion-flies
        Trichoptera    caddis-flies, trout-flies, case-flies
        Lepidoptera    butterflies, moths, skippers, blues, woolly-bears, caterpillars, millers
        Diptera    flies, gnats, mosquitoes, midges, bots, maggots, punkies
        Siphonaptera    fleas, chigoes
        Coleoptera    beetles, weevils, fireflies, elaters, glow-worms, water-pennies, meal-worms, wire-worms, white-grubs

**Class    Subcl    Order**

Strepsiptera    stylopids

Hymenoptera    bees, wasps, ants, sawflies, hornets, wood-wasps,
    ichneumon-flies, gall-wasps, velvet-ants, horntails,
    tarantula-hawks

## CHAETOGNATHA

arrow-worms

SAGITTOIDEA
    Sagittoidea

## POGONOPHORA

beard-worms

POGONOPHORA
        Thecanephria
        Athecanephria

## ECHINODERMATA

echinoderms

CRINOIDEA    feather-stars, crinoids, sea-lilies
    Articulata
        Isocrinida
        Cyrtocrinida
        Comatulida
ASTEROIDEA    starfishes, sea-stars
        Phanerozonea
        Spinulosa
        Forcipulata
OPHIUROIDEA    brittle-stars, sand-stars, basket-stars, serpent-stars
    Myophiurida
        Ophiocystiida
        Aganasterida
        Phrynophiurida
        Laemophiurida
        Gnathophiurida
        Chilophiurida
ECHINOIDEA    sea-urchins, heart-urchins, sand-dollars
    Regularia
        Cidaroida
        Centrechinoida
        Exocycloida

Class    Subcl    Order

Irregularia
    Holectypoida
    Cassiduloida
    Clypeastroida    cake-urchins, sand-dollars
    Spantangoida    heart-urchins
HOLOTHURIOIDEA    sea-cucumbers
    Aspidochirota
    Elasipoda
    Dendrochirota
    Molpadonia
    Apoda

# PTEROBRANCHIA

PTEROBRANCHIA
    Rhabdopleurida
    Cephalodiscidea

# ENTEROPNEUSTA

acorn-worms, tongue-worms

ENTEROPNEUSTA
    Balanoglossida

# PLANCTOSPHAEROIDEA

PLANCTOSPHAEROIDEA
    Planctosphaeroidea

# TUNICATA

tunicates

LARVACEA
    Larvacea
ASCIDIACEA    sea-squirts, ascidians
    Stolidobranchiata
    Aspiraculata
    Phlebobranchiata
    Aplousobranchiata
    Octacnemida
THALIACEA
  Pyrosomata
    Pyrosomatida
  Myosomata
    Cyclomyaria
    Hemimyaria
    Desmomyaria

# CEPHALOCHORDATA

LEPTOCARDIA
   Amphioxi   lancelets

# VERTEBRATA

vertebrates

AGNATHA   [jawless fishes]
   Cephalaspidomorpha
          Cyclostomata   lampreys, hag-fishes, slime-eels
CHONDRICHTHYES   [cartilaginous fishes]
   Elasmobranchii
          Selachii   sharks, dogfishes, angel-fishes
          Batoidea   skates, rays
       Holocephali   rabbit-fishes
          Chimaerae   chimaeras, ratfishes
OSTEICHTHYES   [bony fishes]
   Actinopterygii   [ray-finned fishes]
          Chondrostei
          Holostei   gars
          Teleostei
   Choanichthyes   [lobe-finned fishes]
          Crossopterygii   coelacanths, etc.
          Dipnoi   lungfishes
AMPHIBIA (*Batrachia*)   amphibians, batrachians
   Salientia
          Anura   frogs, toads
   Lepospondyli
          Urodela   salamanders, newts
          Apoda (*Gymnophiona*)   caecilians
REPTILIA   reptiles
   Anapsida
          Chelonia   tortoises, turtles
   Diapsida
          Rhynchocephalia
          Squamata   lizards, snakes
          Crocodilia   crocodiles, gavials, alligators, caymans
AVES   birds
   Neornithes
          Sphenisci (*Sphenisciformes*)   penguins
          Struthiones (*Struthioniformes*)   ostriches

Class    Subcl    Order

Rheae (*Rheiformes*)   rheas

Casuarii (*Casuariiformes*)   cassowaries, emus

Apteryges (*Apterygiformes*)   kiwis

Crypturi (*Crypturiformes, Tinami, Tinamiformes*)   tinamous

Gaviae (*Gaviiformes*)   loons

Podicipedes (*Podicipediformes, Colymbae, Colymbiformes*)
  grebes, divers

Procellariae (*Procellariiformes, Tubinares*)   albatrosses,
  shearwaters, petrels, fulmars,

Steganopodes (*Pelecani, Pelecaniformes*)   cormorants,
  pelicans, gannets, tropicbirds, boobies, snake-birds,
  frigate-birds

Ciconiae (*Ciconiiformes*)   herons, bitterns, storks,
  hammerheads, spoonbills, ibises, flamingoes

Anseres (*Anseriformes*)   ducks, geese, swans, screamers

Falcones (*Falconiformes*)   hawks, eagles, vultures, falcons,
  caracaras, ospreys, harriers, secretary-birds

Galli (*Galliformes*)   megapodes, pheasants, quails, grouse,
  turkeys, fowls, peacocks, hoatzins

Grues (*Gruiformes*)   cranes, limpkins, rails, sunbitterns,
  bustard-quails, plainwanderers, trumpeters, coots, gallinules,
  kagus, sungrebes, bustards

Charadriae (*Charadriiformes*)   jacanas, snipe, oyster-catchers,
  plovers, turnstones, surf-birds, woodcock, sandpipers,
  avocets, stilts, phalaropes, gulls, terns, skimmers, awks,
  murres

Columbae (*Columbiformes*)   doves, pigeons, dodos,
  sandgrouse, solitaires

Psittaci (*Psittaciformes*)   parrots, parakeets, lories, macaws

Cuculi (*Cuculiformes*)   cuckoos, plantain-eaters, touracos,
  anis, roadrunners

Striges (*Strigiformes*)   owls

Caprimulgi (*Caprimulgiformes*)   goatsuckers, potoos,
  oil-birds, frogmouths

Macrochires (*Macrochiriformes, Apoda, Micropodi*)   swifts,
  humming-birds

Colii (*Coliiformes*)   mouse-birds, colies

Trogones (*Trogoniformes*)   trogans

Coraciae (*Coraciiformes*)   kingfishers, rollers, hoopoes,
  hornbills, todies, motmots, bee-eaters

Pici (*Piciformes*)   woodpeckers, toucans, honey-guides,
  jacamars, puffbirds, barbets, piculets

Passeres (*Passeriformes*)   songbirds, warblers, thrushes,
    shrikes, creepers, nuthatches, titmice, vireos, finches,
    tanagers, blackbirds, starlings, orioles, crows, jays, magpies
    swallows, butcher-birds, wrens, thrashers, mockingbirds,
    kinglets, flycatchers, wrentits, dippers, honey-creepers,
    grosbeaks, buntings, broadbills, woodhewers, antbirds,
    ovenbirds, lyrebirds, bulbuls, larks, babblers, wagtails,
    waxwings, weaverbirds, drongos, wattlebirds, bowerbirds,
    birds-of-paradise, etc.

# MAMMALIA   mammals

## Prototheria

Monotremata   monotremes, platypus, echidna

## Metatheria

Marsupialia   marsupials, opossums, Tasmanian-wolf,
    bandicoots, phalangers, koalas, kangaroos

## Eutheria (*Placentalia*)   placentals

Insectivora   insectivores, tenrecs, hedgehogs, shrews

Dermoptera   colugos, flying-lemurs

Chiroptera   bats, vampires

Primates   lemurs, tree-shrews, aye-aye, lorises, bush-babies,
    tarsiers, monkeys, marmosets, macaques, baboons, guenons,
    langurs, apes, gibbons, lars, chimpanzees, orangutans, gorillas,
    men

Edentata   sloths, anteaters, armadillos

Pholidota   pangolins

Lagomorpha   hares, rabbits, pikas

Rodentia   squirrels, chipmunks, marmots, pocket-mice, pacas,
    kangaroo-rats, beavers, rats, mice, muskrats, lemmings, voles,
    dormice, porcupines, capybaras, guinea-pigs, chinchillas

Cetacea   porpoises, dolphins, whales

Carnivora   dogs, wolves, foxes, bears, raccoons, coatis,
    kinkajous, pandas, weasels, minks, otters, badgers,
    wolverines, skunks, civets, hyenas, cats, seals, sea-lions,
    walruses

Tubulidentata   aardvarks

Proboscidea   mastodons, mammoths, elephants

Hyracoidea   hyraxes

Sirenia   sea-cows

Perissodactyla   horses, zebras, tapirs, rhinoceroses

Artiodactyla   pigs, peccaries, hippopotamuses, camels, llamas,
    alpacas, guanacos, deer, giraffes, pronghorns, cattle,
    antelopes, sheep, gazelles, musk-oxen, goats, etc.

# Notes on the Taxa

## Subkingdoms and their subdivisions

*Animalia.* Division of the Animal Kingdom into four subkingdoms is seen in many recent classifications, although some writers prefer to list the Parazoa, Mesozoa, and Eumetazoa as branches of Metazoa in contrast to the Protozoa. The use of the additional level "branch" is difficult to justify where so few groups are involved, unless there is definite information on the phylogeny of these groups. Such knowledge of the relationships of the groups is lacking, or, at best, highly speculative. The groups are generally recognized at the phylum and subkingdom levels, and these seem to be adequate for classification except within the Metazoa proper (see below).

Inasmuch as it is often stated that animals are either one-celled or many-celled, it would seem to be necessary to accept the older subdivision of Animalia into two subkingdoms, Protozoa and Metazoa. The fact is, however, that many undoubted protozoans exist only in aggregations of many cells, often with as much division of labor between cell types as in some undoubted metazoans. Removal of the Protozoa to a separate kingdom Protista solves part of this problem, but the remaining animals still represent the three very different basic structures: 1] a vase-like cylinder open at one end and with several types of cells in the walls but with the internal cavity not serving for digestion, 2] a solid body consisting of one layer of cells around a central cell or group of cells, and 3] a multicellular body with internal cavities of which one is usually a digestive tract and with walls of one, two, or three layers of cells.

These three types of construction are so different as to require recognition as primary divisions of the kingdom. With the Protozoa (when these are treated as animals), they form the four subkingdoms employed here: Eozoa, Parazoa, Agnotozoa, and Histozoa.

*Eozoa* and *Agnotozoa*. In the choice of names for subkingdoms, it has been felt that only slight advantage results from having a single phylum known by a different name than is used for its subkingdom. However, with only four subkingdoms involved and with two of these consisting of two or more phyla, it appears to be reasonable to be uniform in this respect and use separate names for the subkingdom and phylum that include the protozoans and for the subkingdom and phylum that include the mesozoans.

*Parazoa.* The Porifera have long been recognized as constituting a group distinct from the rest of the many-celled animals. The extinct Cyathospongia, under one of the three available names, were placed with the sponges by Okulitch and others, and as a separate phylum in the Parazoa by Pearse and others.

*Histozoa.* This name is accepted here because of the great ambiguity of the more familiar name Metazoa. As explained above, the incorporation of many cells into one body is not distinctive of any major group of animals, even if single-celled adult structure is found exclusively in one group. It was the desire to retain Metazoa which has led many writers to list the Parazoa, Mesozoa, and Eumetazoa as branches of a subkingdom Metazoa. Inasmuch as Metazoa cannot be effectively defined, to the exclusion of all Protozoa, it seems to be more realistic to recognize three or four subkingdoms of animals on the basis of the general body construction. Attempts to divide it on the basis of cell number are arbitrary and misleading.

The use of any of these subkingdom groups is of questionable value; it is the phyla that are important and that are most often definable. The distinction between even Protozoa and Metazoa is so completely nebulous that it no longer serves any clear purpose. Use of the subkingdom and series names herein is simply a recognition of their use in many recent classifications.

Division of the Histozoa (Metazoa) into grades, series, or divisions has been attempted many times. Most of the groups so adopted in the past are employed in the face of obvious defects in the form of exceptions. Not all Radiata show any form of radial arrangement, and not all radially arranged animals are put in the Radiata. Bilateria included animals with quite diverse body plans, some with virtually no paired structures, no obvious "sides," no anterior and posterior, and only a remote similarity to the obviously bilateral animals. Some groups placed in the Schizocoela form their coelom in the enterocoelous manner, and at least one group placed in the Enterocoela forms its coelom by the schizocoelous method. Articulata has included animals that are *not* segmented. And so on.

It is here concluded that the histozoan (or eumetazoan) phyla cannot be grouped readily into clear-cut series. The number of these phyla is not so great as to force subdivision of the subkingdom, but custom seems to be sufficient justification for indicating some grouping of them. At this

point it appears that the most useful grouping is the one based on the *type* of body cavity. Accordingly four groups are here recognized, those phyla with an enterocoel or gastrovascular cavity only, those with no cavities except a digestive tract, those with a pseudocoel, and those with a coelom. These groupings are all well known from Hyman (1940) and other works.

No satisfactory name exists for the first of these four groups. Radiata is inapplicable to many forms. Protaxonia is based on a concept of embryonic axes which would include extraneous groups. Enterozoa and Enterocoela were originally applied to much larger concepts. On the whole, Enterocoela is the most appropriate in meaning, and it is adopted here.

*Radiata* and *Bilateria*. The Histozoa or Metazoa have sometimes been divided into the Radiata (Coelenterata and Ctenophora) and the Bilateria (all others) on the basis of their general body arrangement. The distinction is here held to be a fictitious one, because Ctenophora are much less radial than some Echinodermata, and such an animal as a bryozoan is so completely different in body arrangement from an annelid worm that it is meaningless to say that they are both bilateral.

## Phyla and rejected phylum groups

*Cyathospongia*. Recent works on this extinct phylum have adopted either Pleospongia or Archaeocyatha as the phylum name. Both of these names are of later date (1937) than Cyathospongia (1935), and Archaeocyatha has been used more consistently for one of the included classes. There seems to be no firmly established usage that prevents us adopting the oldest name.

*Mesozoa*. There appears to be no reason for not adopting the name now in wide use for this phylum, especially as it is the oldest name (1877). The name has also been used at the subkingdom level, where the synonym Agnotozoa seems to be more appropriate.

*Monoblastozoa*. A new phylum named here for the unique metazoan *Salinella*, which has too long been left excluded from the classifications of animals. It contains only one genus and one species. The animal consists of a single layer of similar cells surrounding an internal tubular tract which has a "mouth" at one end, an "anus"

at the other. The cells are thus simultaneously both "ectoderm" and "endoderm"; they are ciliated on both surfaces. Reproduction is asexual (by transverse fission), and there are indications of a sexual process in the form of fusion of two individuals. It is possible that a ciliated unicellular larva results from the sexual process.

Hyman suggested (1940) the phylum status for this peculiar animal, but she did not propose such a phylum directly and left *Salinella* unassigned to any group.

*Graptozoa*. The graptolites have had a more varied history than most other major groups. They were for years assigned to the Hydrozoa in the Coelenterata, but have more recently been transferred to the Hemichordata. In 1959 Hyman examined the arguments supporting the hemichordate assignment. After effectively disposing of all of these, she left the group without clear assignment, although she presumably retained them in the Hydrozoa, as she had doubtfully done in 1940.

Some features of the skeleton of graptolites are not duplicated in the Hydrozoa, and the nature of the material of this exoskeleton is not known. It is not possible to say definitely that the graptolites are coelenterates, because the nature of the body cavity is not known, but there is no evidence that it is not a coelenteron. The graptolites may thus reasonably be included in the Coelenterata, even placed in the Hydrozoa because of general similarities, but information is simply lacking that would enable one to say that they did have the features of the coelenterates.

Inasmuch as there is some evidence of bilaterality, the skeletal tubes are different from those of Hydrozoa in manner of formation, and the almost universal form of the colonies is unmatched in the Hydrozoa, it is also reasonable to emphasize the differences by separating the group from the Hydrozoa as a class. Because of the lack of knowledge of all soft-part features and the possibility that some of these also are without counterpart in the Coelenterata, it is here preferred to emphasize this uncertainty by separating the group as a phylum distinct from Coelenterata.

The class Hydrozoa is already one of the most diverse in the Animal Kingdom. It seems undesirable to increase further its heterogeneity by including an additional series of different features. The distinctive features of the Coelenterata cannot be adduced to help us with the graptolites, so these fossils cannot be included in that phylum upon any firm basis.

*Conularida.* The same arguments as applied above to the Graptozoa are cogent for the separation of the Conularida as a separate phylum also. Apparently no coelenterates have a chitinophosphatic skeleton, which fact alone makes the inclusion of these animals in that phylum unsatisfactory. Of course, here also there is no direct evidence that the animals were actually coelenterate in nature.

This group has recently been assigned to the Scyphozoa, although also placed sometimes as a phylum near the Annelida or as a member of some other phylum. Although quite easily restored to look very much like elongate scyphozoans, the fossil remains of these animals show consistent differences in the steep-sided pyramidal form with four distinct sides, the closing of the aperture by lobes of the side faces, and the chitinophosphatic nature of the periderm. The arguments in the Treatise (F) for combining these with the Scyphozoa seem very weak.

*Coelenterata.* In some recent works (especially Hyman, 1940) this phylum has been called Cnidaria because Coelenterata has at other times included such groups as Ctenophora and Porifera. This reason for abandoning the universally known name Coelenterata would, if applied to other modern phylum concepts, result in changing most of the familiar names, including Porifera, Annelida, Arthropoda, Hemichordata, and Chordata. Such a change cannot, in the opinion of the writer, be justified by any benefits resulting therefrom. If it is thought to be necessary, the prior name Nematozoa would also have to be considered. (Furthermore, inclusion of the Graptozoa or Conularida (as in Hyman) would likewise necessitate a change in the phylum name, by this same argument.)

*Aschelminthes.* The proposal of this name by Hyman (1940) for all of the Pseudocoelomata except the Entoprocta has been adopted by some later works, but her alternate conclusion that the subphyla each be treated as a separate phylum has also been followed by some. It is surely premature to claim that the Aschelminthes has been conclusively accepted. Hyman (1951) removes one of the original seven groups (Acanthocephala) as a separate phylum.

The definition given for the emended phylum Aschelminthes in 1951 contains no clear-cut distinctions. Unless such exist, the supposed phylum must be concluded to be an indefinable assemblage. The fact that the included subgroups are mostly small and less well known is of no value in determining whether they are phyla, subphyla, or classes. It is here believed that they are adequately distinct by clear-cut features of fundamental nature (body plan, ciliation, "segmentation" of cuticle, presence of jaws, presence of flame bulbs or solenocytes, musculature, nature of nervous system, etc.) to be considered separate phyla.

*Nemathelminthes* and *Trochelminthes.* These two names were formerly applied to the thread-like and the ciliated animals more recently combined into the Aschelminthes. These groupings are also difficult to define. It is therefore preferred to treat their components as separate phyla. Nemathelminthes usually included the Nematoda, Gordiacea, Acanthocephala, and sometimes the Chaetognatha. The Trochelminthes included the Rotifera and Gastrotricha.

*Nematoda.* Hyman is followed here in rejecting recent proposals to change this name to Nemata.

*Gordiacea.* The best form of this name at the phylum level is a moot question. Little is gained but confusion by using Nematomorpha, whereas Gordioidea has generally been used at the class or order level. Gordiacea seems to remain as the most distinctive phylum name.

*Calyssozoa / Endoprocta.* Entoprocta is accepted by Hyman for this group, but this name (or the more distinctive spelling Endoprocta) is much more often applied at the class level. Calyssozoa was proposed originally (and followed by Kamptozoa) for the group as a phylum. Inasmuch as names are needed at both levels, Calyssozoa is accepted here for the phylum and Endoprocta for the single class. (The spellings Endoprocta and Entoprocta are both ascribed to Nitsche (1870). Both have been used extensively, but the former is more distinct from Ectoprocta and is therefore adopted here.)

*Myzostomida.* This peculiar and little-known group has previously been listed as a class of Annelida, as a subclass of Chaetopoda, or as part of the Polychaeta, but apparently never as a phylum.

These animals are disc-shaped, are non-segmented although with some paired organs, have five pairs of ventral appendages and four pairs of suckers, have ten or more pairs of marginal cirri or tentacles, lack blood-vascular and respiratory systems as well as multiple nephridia, have the central nervous system consisting of a single large ventral stellate ganglion and two nerve rings around the oesophagus and pharynx, have a complete digestive tract but with the stomach branching throughout the body, and have a trochosphere larva. These features would make the Annelida impossible to diagnose, and they result in an animal whose peculiarities are only obscured by inclusion in the Annelida.

Prenant (1960) in the Traité concludes that these animals are annelids but sufficiently distinct to be made a class. It is here believed that the features cited by Prenant make it necessary to remove the Myzostomida from the Annelida, just as the Sipunculoidea and Echiuroidea had previously been removed.

Myzostomids are reported from several geologic eras. As these are known only from scars or galls, they cannot be assigned to orders. **69758**

*Protarthropoda.* The inclusion of Tardigrada, Onychophora, and Pentastomida in the Arthropoda as a subphylum (Protarthropoda, Pararthropoda, or Oncopoda) has been done, in every case traced out, without direct consideration of whether they have the basic features of arthropods, or whether the resulting agglomeration can be defined. Apparently it cannot be defined, and these three groups individually have only a few of the basic arthropod features. Until more correlation is demonstrated, it is held that they cannot reasonably be combined with the Arthropoda.

*Tardigrada.* This group is generally placed in either the Aschelminthes or the Arthropoda. Either position is untenable if Cuenot (1949) is correct in asserting that the animals are coelomate and enterocoelous. It is distinguished from Onychophora and Pentastomida, as well as Arthropoda, by features of considerable importance. It is certainly entitled to phylum status, even if the correct position for the phylum is still unknown.

*Pentastomida.* This group is generally placed in the Arthropoda, sometimes even in the order Acarida. Some of its characters have been ascribed to parasitic degeneration. They apparently have no cilia, do have a chitinous cuticle, and do have an arthropod type of nervous system. They lack an exoskeleton, jointed appendages, Malpighian tubules or coxal glands, circulatory organs, tracheae, and nephridia, and their appendages are of the type seen in the Onychophora and the Tardigrada.

As it would be impossible to place these definitely in any class of arthropods, and since they lack many arthropod features, it seems best to emphasize their differences by treating them as a separate phylum.

*Hemichordata (Branchiotremata, Adelochorda).* Nearly all recent classifications recognize a phylum Hemichordata that includes the Enteropneusta, the Pterobranchia, and perhaps such other groups as the Graptozoa. A good example of this is Hyman (1959). It is difficult to understand this grouping when every attempt at definition consists primarily of variable or relative characters. The components are so distinct that Hyman can only discuss them separately. Almost none of her statements apply throughout the phylum.

In this situation we only obscure the

diversity and the differences by pretending that they can be included in one phylum. Besides the Enteropneusta and the Pterobranchia, there have been placed here also the Planctosphaeroidea, the Phoronida, and the Graptozoa. The latter two have already been accepted as distinct phyla in a previous part of this classification (following many other classifications). The Planctosphaeroidea, consisting of certain ciliated larvae of unknown affinities, cannot be associated with any known adults. It is therefore impossible to combine them confidently with any phylum. It seems necessary to maintain them as a distinct group at the present time.

*Chordata.* It is now more than seventy-five years since the vertebrates and some supposed relatives were first combined under this name. Nearly all subsequent classifications have accepted this arrangement, although the included groups vary somewhat. At the extreme the Chordata have included the Hemichordata, Tunicata, and Cephalochordata, as well as the Vertebrata.

The inclusion of the Hemichordata is unequivocally rejected by Hyman (1959) and others. The arguments seem to be well founded, involving the absence of any substantial similarity in major features.

The Tunicata, included in the Chordata as a matter of course in many works, are excluded here because the similarities appear to be far outweighed by the differences between tunicates and vertebrates. Even if an homologous notochord be present, even if perforations of the tracheal walls do occur, the extreme differences in arrangement of the digestive tract, the absence of paired structures in tunicates, the presence of the tunic and the substance tunicin in tunicates, the reversible blood flow in tunicates, and so on, all seem to deny a similarity so close as to justify inclusion in one phylum. With the tunicates included, the Chordata are extremely difficult to define effectively, except on the two features of notochord and pharyngotremy. With the tunicates excluded, the list of features held in common by the remaining groups is considerably increased.

The Cephalochordata can much more reasonably be united with the vertebrates. Nevertheless, the oral hood, the atrial system, the brown funnel, the multiple paired solenocytic nephridia, the single-layered epidermis, the peculiar liver-pouch, the absence of a heart, the multiple ductless gonads, and other features seem to show that the group is "more widely separated from the lowest fish than the lowest fish from a bird or mammal" (Parker & Haswell, 1897). It seems appropriate to recognize these substantial differences at the phylum level.

The use of the name Chordata for the restricted concept seems to be unnecessary as well as inappropriate. The name is younger and less well known than Vertebrata. It would seem to be an unnecessary name, based on overemphasis on a very few features held in common by the groups involved. At the most it might be considered to be a sort of "superphylum," but even thus it could reasonably include only the Cephalochordata and the Vertebrata.

## Sources of class and order arrangements

*Protozoa.* The five classes of Protozoa are almost universally agreed upon in recent works. The use of the subphyla is not so widespread. Protociliata may be considered to belong in the Plasmodroma rather than in the Ciliophora, being there treated as a separate class. Suctoria are sometimes united with Ciliata as a subclass. Telosporidia (Amoebosporidia) are sometimes separated from Sporozoa as a third subphylum.

This is the classification of Kudo (1954) except for: 1] the elevation of Haplosporidia and Sarcosporidia to subclass level, following Hyman (1940); and 2] a few cases of different choice from available synonyms.

*Porifera.* Three classes are recognized in most recent works, including the Treatise of Invertebrate Paleontology (E, 1955), but most paleontology books list also the Receptaculitida as *incertae sedis*. Inasmuch as it cannot be justified in any of the three classes, it must stand as a separate class. (The Nidulitida are now thought to be algae rather than sponges, and the Pleospongea are treated as a separate phylum).

Many works divide each of the three classes into subclasses. In some cases these subclasses are based on features now believed to be of minor importance or taxonomic value, and the view of de Laubenfels is here adopted that subclasses do not add effectively to the classification of this group. Aside from this, the arrangement here adopted is substantially that of both Hyman and the Treatise (E).

*Cyathospongia.* The status and subdivisions of this extinct phylum are taken from Okulitch in the Treatise (E, 1955). The oldest of the three names for the phylum is accepted here. (Archaeocyatha remains as a class).

*Mesozoa.* In adopting this phylum most of the views of Hyman (1940) are accepted, except that the two orders are deemed to be amply distinct in basic development and histology to be treated as classes. This is the arrangement of Lankester (1901). It is also believed that Lankester was justified in separating the Heterocyemida from the other Dicyemida, and they are accordingly given ordinal rank; for this class the name Rhombozoa is available.

*Monoblastozoa.* (See remarks under Phyla, above.)

*Graptozoa.* The orders are taken from the Treatise (V, 1955).

*Conularida.* This arrangement is taken from the Treatise (F, 1956), but the treatment as a phylum is new here (see remarks under Phyla, above).

*Coelenterata.* The classification of the classes of this phylum adopted here is the usual one except for two features: 1] two extinct classes are added, and 2] one group often listed as an order or subclass is given class rank. The first two classes are dealt with as in the Treatise (F). The third one requires discussion here.

Stromatoporoidea. This group has recently been included in the Hydrozoa. The principal arguments in favor of this seem to be that there are other Hydrozoa showing some of the same peculiar colonial features. It appears that this is an argument for re-examining these other groups (such as Spongiomorphida), because their preserved hard-parts show few features of Recent Hydrozoa. It seems best to emphasize the considerable structural differences between stromatoporoids and typical hydrozoans by not merging them in one class.

The only reasons that can be given for retaining the stromatoporoids in the Coelenterata while removing the graptolites from that phylum are that the graptolites form a somewhat more distinct group and that the recent extreme divergence in views on their position in the Animal Kingdom lend credence to their more isolated position. Retention of the stromatoporoids does not at present alter the definition of the Hydrozoa.

The orders of Stromatoporoidea are accepted from Shrock & Twenhofel (1953) after Kuhn (1939). Other recent works divide the group into families, using no orders. The orders of Hydrozoa are those of Hyman (1940) plus the extinct Spongiomorphida. The orders of Scyphozoa are those of Hyman (1940) plus the extinct Lithorhizostomeae, being thus those listed in the Treatise (F) after the removal of the Conularida. The orders of Anthozoa are those of the Treatise, and they are those of Hyman (1940) except for the Ceriantipatharia and the extinct orders.

*Ctenophora.* The classification of Hyman (1940) is accepted both as to classes and orders. Nearly all recent works agree on this arrangement.

*Platyhelminthes.* Three classes are generally recognized here, but the most recent monographic work on the tapeworms (Wardle & McLeod, 1952) seems to justify the recognition of the Cestodaria as a class distinct from the Cestoda. Hyman (1951) included these in the Cestoda as a subclass, but she found them sufficiently distinct to require separate treatment in all respects from the rest of the tapeworms (Eucestoda).

At one time the Temnocephaloidea were treated as a class intermediate between Turbellaria and Trematoda. Although it has been claimed that this arrangement is now abandoned by all workers, it does reappear in Dawes' (1946) monographic study of the Trematoda. In deference to Hyman's studies on the Turbellaria, the group is herein placed in the Turbellaria as a suborder of Rhabdocoela.

The orders of Trematoda are taken from Dawes (1946), of Cestoda and Cestodaria from Wardle & McLeod (1952), and of Turbellaria from Hyman (1951).

*Rhynchocoela.* Many recent works have divided this phylum into two classes, the Enopla and the Anopla. While accepting this subdivision, Hyman (1951) considers "the great similarity of structure throughout the phylum" as reason for not making these two groups classes. She therefore lists them as subclasses, there being no class mentioned. There is no rule preventing the subdivision of a phylum directly into subclasses, but it is unfamiliar and disconcerting.

The features cited by Hyman as distinguishing the two subclasses seem to be no more fundamental than those used for distinguishing the orders. It is therefore here considered preferable to consider the nemertines as consisting of a single class of four orders. (The orders are those cited by Hyman, 1951.)

Inasmuch as there are two well-known names available for this one-class phylum, it seems reasonable to retain one for the phylum and the other for the class. There is little reason to choose either way, but Hyman's argument that Schultze (1850–51) was the "zoologist who first clearly understood the group" may be used as justification for adopting Schultze's name, Rhynchocoela, for the phylum.

*Acanthocephala.* This is another one-class phylum, for which no class names are available. The orders are listed as in Hyman (1951).

*Rotifera.* The decision made above, not to employ the Aschelminthes for six groups of pseudocoelomate animals, results in elevation of these six groups to phyla. This raises the question of whether the orders of the former class Rotifera should be raised to classes. This has been done by some classifiers, but there is considerable hesitation to doing so here. The Seisonidea appear from Hyman's remarks to be sufficiently distinct to be considered a separate class, but it is not so clear that Bdelloidea and Monogononta can be distinguished by equally fundamental characters. In this dilemma, the three groups are tentatively treated as classes, with the three groups within the Monogononta treated as orders.

*Gastrotricha.* The differences between the two groups of gastrotrichs, as described by Hyman, including the protonephridia, pharyngeal pores, and the body cavity subdivision, appear to justify the elevation of the two groups to the level of classes. Each then consists of a single order.

*Kinorhyncha.* Although this group is here considered to be a distinct phylum rather than a class of Aschelminthes, there seems to be no reason for not following Hyman (1951) in considering its subdivisions as of less than ordinal rank. The characters distinguishing the three subdivisions are principally matters of degree, including no fundamental clear-cut distinctions.

As the phylum must contain at least one class, there seems to be no reason for not using the name Echinodera at this level. It remains effectively a synonym of Kinorhyncha.

*Priapuloidea.* The three known species belong to two genera. There appears to be no basis for separating these at the ordinal level (Hyman, 1951), and therefore there is a single class with one order.

*Nematoda.* Although the treatment of this group as a phylum differs from Hyman's (1951) treatment of it as a class of Aschelminthes, her view is accepted that there are no subdivisions worthy of rank above the ordinal level. The single class can be distinguished from the phylum by the older but less familiar spelling Nematoidea.

*Gordiacea.* There appears to be little of basic nature in the differences between the Gordioidea and the Nectonematoidea. Hyman (1951) is therefore followed in placing these as orders, although in the status of the group as a whole a different view is adopted (see Aschelminthes, above).

*Calyssozoa / Endoprocta.* A single class and order make up this phylum, and the only questions which arise are about the names to be used. The order has been called Pedicellinida by Boettger (1952), the name Entoprocta or Endoprocta has generally been used for the class, and the first name proposed for the phylum is Calyssozoa of Clark (1921). It seems least confusing to accept these rather than duplicate one name at several levels. (The spelling Endoprocta is here preferred over Entoprocta because of its greater difference from Ectoprocta.

*Bryozoa.* Hyman's (1959) division of this phylum into two classes with six orders, following many earlier workers, is accepted here, as in most current paleontological works.

The single order of the Phylactolaemata seems to be without a name. The name first used for the group was Lophopoda, abandoned by later workers in favor of Phylactolaemata. It is here revived for the ordinal level.

The argument for replacing Bryozoa with Ectoprocta because of removal of the Endoprocta has been answered above under Coelenterata. Removal of one group is not considered justification for changing the name of a phylum (or other taxon).

*Phoronida.* The two genera seem to belong to a single order, for which there is no special name (Hyman, 1959).

*Brachiopoda.* There appears to be universal agreement as to the division of this phylum into two classes. Six pairs of names have been proposed for these classes, of which Inarticulata and Articulata are favored in most recent works. The Inarticulata are usually divided into two orders, and the Articulata were formerly divided into two or three orders. There is no general agreement on the orders of Articulata, and the opinion of Hyman (1959) and others that there is no satisfactory classification is accepted here. However, one of the older orders is still acceptable to paleontologists, and there is no satisfactory method for combining the remaining two. The older division into three orders is therefore followed, until a clear alternative is available.

*Mollusca.* Only one recent American work is known to list seven classes of Mollusca as is done herein. There is difference of opinion among modern workers only as to the status of the groups sometimes referred to as Isopleura. Many texts have omitted the fossil Monoplacophora and treated the Solenogastres as an *incertae sedis* group. This leaves the Amphineura or Placophora as a fifth class. It also leaves the classification of the phylum incomplete and therefore unsatisfactory.

In volume I of the Treatise of Invertebrate Paleontology, Yonge (1960) discusses the features of these groups and concludes that there are seven classes. This arrangement is followed also in the Traité de Zoologie and is accepted herein.

Monoplacophora. Until 1957 this class was known only as fossils. Its division into three orders is taken from the Treatise (I, 1960).

Amphineura / Polyplacophora. There are three substantially different classifications of this group among recent works. These are: 1] orders Lepidopleurida and Chitonida, by Thiele (1935), etc.; 2] orders Eoplacophora, Mesoplacophora, Isoplacophora, and Teleoplacophora, by Cotton & Godfrey (1940); and 3] orders Paleoloricata and Neoloricata, by Smith (1960). There seems to be little direct correlation between these systems.

Smith's system is ostensibly based on Pilsbry's early classification, modified by paleontological data. It is unfamiliar to neontologists, but it may be readily understood when it is seen that all living chitons are placed in the order Neoloricata (to which many fossil forms belong as well). It is adopted here as the best available classification of a neglected group.

Aplacophora. There appears to be no

disagreement on the division of this class into two orders. It is sometimes treated as a subclass or even as an order, of Amphineura or Gastropoda.

Gastropoda. Nearly all recent writers agree on the division of this class into three subclasses, following Thiele (1931). The first, Prosobranchia, has been widely divided into three orders, but Cox (1960) in the Treatise (I), has combined two of these under the new name Caenogastropoda. His new arrangement is followed here, although in other respects Thiele's classification is accepted. A recent classification by Taylor & Sohl (1962) is not followed here because it is not accompanied by justification at the ordinal level.

Bivalvia / Pelecypoda. A considerable variety of classifications are in use for this class, with little obvious correlation of groupings. At the present time it appears best to present the more common arrangement of neontologists and also the customary paleontological one (in the footnotes), until a single scheme has been accepted by both groups of workers. The first of these is the scheme of Lankester (1906) and most later textbooks. The second is the scheme of Cotton & Godfrey (1938) with the orders raised to subclasses as by Cox (1960). (Cox's more numerous orders may represent a more natural arrangement, but it is not yet known whether they will be acceptable to other workers.)

Scaphopoda. Apparently no names are available for the single class and the single order. Therefore, Scaphopoda is here used for all three levels, as they are coextensive.

Cephalopoda. There is little agreement among recent workers as to the subdivision of this class, although many of the subgroups are found in all schemes. The arrangement followed here is that of Cotton & Godfrey (1940) and many of the older textbooks. The numerous nautiloid "orders" of Flower & Kümmel (1950) are based largely on relative characters and have not been clearly established as entitled to ordinal rank.

*Sipunculoidea.* The ten genera of this phylum are not separated into classes or orders. Separate names are not available for the resulting single class and order.

*Echiuroidea.* This phylum, which has often been placed in or appended to the Annelida, is divided into two classes as in Boettger (1952). The class Echiurida is divided into three orders as in Pearse (1949).

*Myzostomida.* The two orders are accepted from Prenant in the Traité de Zoologie (1959).

*Annelida.* Many recent books list the Polychaeta and Oligochaeta as separate classes. The differences between the two are largely relative, and the two together can be described in detail with few conflicts. For this reason, the two groups are here combined in the class Chaetopoda, as in many of the older works. Their differences may then be brought out at the subclass level.

No really satisfactory classification of this phylum or its classes has been found.

Polychaeta. The usual division into two orders has been followed, with the addition of one extinct order.

Oligochaeta. There being no generally accepted subdivision of this group, the one given without Latin names by Avel (1959) in the Traité (attributed by him to Michaelson, 1930) and without acceptable single names by Pearse (1949) is followed here. The names are emended to conform to custom in Latin nomenclature.

Hirudinea. Division of this class into four orders was proposed by Harant & Grassé (1959) using three orders proposed by Caballero (1952) and adding the "Acanthobdelliformes nom.nov." These names and groupings were not new there, except in ending. Rhynchobdellida dates from Blanchard (1887), Gnathobdellida from Vaillant (1890), and Pharyngobdellida from Johannson (1913). These same four orders were recognized by Lowenstein (1954), using the name Acanthobdellida and using the name Herpobdellida instead of Pharyngobdelliformes.

It is not clear whether these names were independently proposed, but there seems to be no need for the *-iformes* endings here. The four orders are accepted here, the spellings of Caballero and of Harant & Grassé are rejected, and Pharyngobdellida is accepted because of apparent priority.

Archiannelida. There is apparently general agreement that there is only one order in this class. No ordinal name is available.

*Tardigrada.* The division into three orders in two classes is taken from Pearse (1949), after Richters (1926) and Marcus (1927).

*Pentastomida.* The orders are from Boettger (1952).

*Onychophora.* Division of the phylum into two orders is accepted from Boettger (1952) and the Treatise (O, 1959), following earlier writers.

*Arthropoda.* Some recent classifications of this largest of all phyla have been complicated by attempts to include the Pentastomida, Onychophora, and even the Tardigrada. When this is done, the phylum can no longer be defined, because it would include a variety of body cavities, nervous systems, respiratory systems, excretory systems, integuments, etc. With these groups removed, the arthropods can readily be classified into eleven classes, and these can be grouped into three subphyla.

Much of the classification of the Arthropoda above the ordinal level is in an unsettled state. There seems to be no single complete classification that is adequate for both Recent and fossil groups. The one presented here is therefore made up from many sources, most of which are at least in part drawn from earlier sources. Listed below are the recent works that are accepted at each level, but they usually are not the original proposal of the arrangement.

Subphyla are accepted from Pearse (1949), classes in the Trilobitomorpha from the Treatise (O, 1959), in the Chelicerata from Pearse (1949) and Moore (1952), and in the Mandibulata from Pearse (1949) with exclusion of superclasses.

Orders in the Trilobitomorpha are from the Treatise (O, 1959), in the Merostomata from the Treatise (P, 1955), in the Pycnogonida from the Treatise (P, 1955), in the Arachnida from the Treatise (P, 1955) which is the system of Petrunkevitch, in the Crustacea from Waterman & Chace (1960), in the Pauropoda and Symphyla from Brues & Melander (1954), in the Diplopoda from Boettger (1952), in the Chilopoda from Pearse (1949), and in the Insecta from Brues & Melander (1954).

The class Eurypterida consists of a single order, for which the synonym Gigantostraca can reasonably be used.

*Chaetognatha.* This is another of the one-class one-order phyla. Boettger (1952) has used the name Sagittoidea for both class and order, but it seems to be more appropriate to restrict this name to the ordinal level and to use the phylum name also at the class level. The other two synonyms seem to be inappropriate as they were originally employed in somewhat different context.

*Pogonophora.* This is probably the newest phylum in point of knowledge of the animals themselves, as the first species was described in 1914, and most of the present day knowledge is less than a score of years old. Only one classification has been undertaken, by Ivanov (1955), and his division into two orders is accepted here.

Inasmuch as the synonym Brachiata is not well known for these animals, it has not been used for the one class.

*Echinodermata.* No single satisfactory classification has been found for this varied phylum. The subphyla here accepted (see footnotes) are those of Shrock & Twenhofel (1953). The classes in the Pelmatozoa, Homalozoa, and Haplozoa are those of Shrock & Twenhofel (1953), being extinct except for the Crinoidea; in the Eleutherozoa the scheme of Shrock & Twenhofel is modified according to the views of Hyman (1955) to omit the Stelleroidea and treat Asteroidea and Ophiuroidea as classes. This makes it necessary also to treat as classes the extinct groups Auluroidea and Somasteroidea. This arrangement is admittedly a compromise with more familiar classifications.

This phylum contains a large number of extinct subgroups, and it is difficult to give full attention to the extinct subgroups without confusing the classification of Recent ones. The orders accepted here are as follows: In Pelmatozoa, Homalozoa, and Haplozoa, from Shrock & Twenhofel (1953); in Asteroidea, from Hyman (1955); in Ophiuroidea, from Boettger (1952) except for removal of Auluroidea; in Echinoidea, from Shrock & Twenhofel (1953) for the Regularia and from Hyman (1955) for the Irregularia (except for removal of Bothriocidaroida after Moore

et al. (1952); and in the Holothurioidea, from Shrock & Twenhofel (1953).

*Pterobranchia.* Many writers agree on dividing the pterobranchs into two groups. The difficulties of describing *Rhabdopleura* and *Cephalodiscus* together leads to skepticism that they should be considered orders rather than classes. In deference to workers in this field, the usual division is adopted, with some misgivings (as in Hyman, 1959).

*Enteropneusta.* Only one class and one order is known in this group. It is sometimes left without a name, but Balanoglossida is available. It is here used for the order, as the phylum name is also familiar at the class level.

*Planctosphaeroidea.* This phylum consists of a single species of what appear to be larvae.

*Tunicata.* There appears to be general agreement on the assignment of the tunicates to three major classes. The subclasses and orders accepted here are those of Pearse (1949) and others, with addition to the Ascidiacea of an order Octacnemida after Harant (1948).

*Cephalochordata.* This group, which is usually included in the Chordata, has at least four available names. Those adopted are the ones most often used at the respective levels.

*Vertebrata.* The restriction of this phylum to the craniates is explained in a previous section. The classes of Vertebrata are taken from Romer (1945) and Colbert (1955). The orders of these classes are taken from these same works, except that Romer is generally followed where he treats as orders the groups which Colbert lists as subclasses or superorders.

# Complete List

## A N I M A L I A
(Zoa)

EOZOA (*Plastidozoa*)
        Protozoa                                                                CAM-REC
PARAZOA
        Porifera (*Spongiaria, Spongeae*)                        CAM-REC
        Cyathospongia (*Pleospongia, Archaeocyatha*)        CAM
AGNOTOZOA
        Mesozoa (*Planuloidea, Mionelminthes, Moruloidea*    REC
HISTOZOA (*Metazoa, Eumetazoa*)
    Enterocoela (*Enterozoa, Protaxonia*)
        Monoblastozoa                                                    REC
        Graptozoa                                                    CAM-MIS
        Conularida                                                    CAM-TRI
        Coelenterata (*Cnidaria, Nematozoa, Nematophora*)    CAM-REC
        Ctenophora (*Acnidaria, Collaria, Ctenarea, Ctenoph-    REC
            oraria*)
    Acoelomata
        Platyhelminthes (*Platodes*)                            REC
        Rhynchocoela (*Nemertinea, Aplocoela, Miocoela*)    REC
    Pseudocoelomata (*Pseudocoelia, Autoscolecida, Protoneph-
            ridozoa*)
        Acanthocephala                                            REC
        Rotifera (*Rotatoria*)                                    REC
        Gastrotricha                                                REC
        Kinorhyncha (*Echinodera*)                            REC
        Priapuloidea                                                REC
        Nematoda (*Nemata*)                                    REC
        Gordiacea (*Gordioidea, Nematomorpha*)        CAR-REC
        Calyssozoa (*Entoprocta, Endoprocta, Kamptozoa*)    REC

# of Phyla[1]

| Subk | Series | Phylum | |
|---|---|---|---|
| | | Coelomata (*Eucoelomata*) | |
| | | Bryozoa (*Polyzoa, Ectoprocta*) | ORD-REC |
| | | Phoronida | REC |
| | | Brachiopoda (*Spirobranchia, Palliobranchiopoda*) | CAM-REC |
| | | Mollusca (*Palliata, Malacozoa, Saccata, Heterogan- gliata, Otocardia*) | CAM-REC |
| | | Sipunculoidea | REC |
| | | Echiuroidea | REC |
| | | Myzostomida | JUR-REC |
| | | Annelida (*Annulata, Coelhelminthes*) | CAM-REC |
| | | Tardigrada | REC |
| | | Pentastomida (*Linguatulida*) | REC |
| | | Onychophora (*Polypoda, Protracheata, Ceratophora, Malacopoda*) | CAM-REC |
| | | Arthropoda (*Euarthropoda*) | CAM-REC |
| | | Chaetognatha (*Homalopterygia, Oesthelminthes*) | CAM-REC |
| | | Pogonophora (*Brachiata*) | REC |
| | | Echinodermata | CAM-REC |
| | | Pterobranchia | ORD-REC |
| | | Enteropneusta (*Helminthomorpha*) | REC |
| | | Planctosphaeroidea | REC |
| | | Tunicata (*Urochordata*) | REC |
| | | Cephalochordata (*Acrania, Cirrhostomi, Entomocra- nia, Haplocyemata, Homomeria, Myelozoa, Pharyngo- branchii*) | REC |
| | | Vertebrata (*Euchorda, Craniata*) | ORD-REC |

[1] For explanations, see preceding section.

# Complete List of Classes and Orders

## with Synonyms, Subgroups, and Geologic Range

**Class  Subcl  Order**

## P R O T O Z O A [1]

| | | |
|---|---|---:|
| FLAGELLATA [2] (*Mastigophora*) | | SIL-REC |
| Phytomastigina [3] (*Phytomastigophorea*) | | SIL-REC |
| Chrysomonadina (*Silicoflagellata, Chrysomonada-ceae*) | | CRE-REC |
| Coccolithophorida | | SIL-REC |
| Cryptomonadina (*Cryptomonadaceae*) | | REC |
| Phytomonadina (*Volvocales, Volvocina, Volvocaceae*) | | EOC-REC |
| Euglenoidina (*Euglenida, Euglenaceae*) | | EOC-REC |
| Chloromonadina (*Chloromonadaceae*) | | REC |
| Dinoflagellata [4] (*Cilioflagellata, Catenata*) | | JUR-REC |
| Zoomastigina [5] (*Zoomastigophorea*) | | REC |
| Rhizomastigina (*Pantostomatida, Rhizomastigaceae Rhizoflagellata*) | | REC |
| Protomonadina (*Protomastigida, Protomastigaceae*) | | REC |
| Polymastigina | | REC |
| Hypermastigina (*Holomastigina*) | | REC |
| SARCODINA | | CAM-REC |
| Rhizopoda [6] | | ORD-REC |
| Proteomyxa | | REC |

[1] *Synonyms:* Eozoa, Plastidozoa. *Subphyla:* Plasmodroma (Homokaryota, Gymnomyxa, Cytomorpha) = FLAGELLATA + SARCODINA + SPOROZOA. Ciliophora (Infusoria, Heterokaryota, Cytoidea) = CILIATA + SUCTORIA. *Includes:* Corticata (FLAGELLATA + SPOROZOA + CILIOPHORA).

[2] *Includes:* Lissoflagellata, Monadidea, Heteromastigina, Chromomonadina, Choanoflagellata, Craspedomonadina, Phalansteriina, Phytoflagellata, Chlamydomonadina, Euflagellata.

[3] *Includes:* Heterochlorida.

[4] *Includes:* Prorocentraceae, Adinida, Peridiniaceae, Gymnodiniaceae, Diniferidea, Cystoflagellata, Rhynchoflagellata.

[5] *Includes:* Trichomonadida.

[6] *Includes:* Labyrinthulidea, Lobosa, Filosa.

| Class | Subcl | Order | |
|---|---|---|---|
| | | Mycetozoa [7] (*Myxomycetes, Myxogasteres*) | REC |
| | | Amoebozoa (*Amoebina, Amoebaea, Nuda, Gymna-moebaea*) | REC |
| | | Testacea (*Thecamoebae*) | EOC-REC |
| | | Foraminifera [8] (*Reticularia, Polythalamia, Thalamo-phora*) | ORD-REC |
| | Actinopoda | | CAM-REC |
| | | Heliozoa [9] | PLE-REC |
| | | Radiolaria [10] (*Polycystina, Cytophora, Echinocystida*) | CAM-REC |
| SPOROZOA [11] (*Gregarina*) | | | REC |
| | Telosporidia [12] (*Cytosporidia, Ectospora, Amoebosporidea*) | | REC |
| | | Gregarinida [13] | REC |
| | | Coccidia [14] (*Coccidiomorpha*) | REC |
| | | Haemosporidia [15] (*Haemocytozoa, Acystosporidia, Gymnosporidia*) | REC |
| | Cnidosporidia | | REC |
| | | Myxosporidia (*Amoebogeniae*) | REC |
| | | Actinomyxidia | REC |
| | | Microsporidia | REC |
| | | Helicosporidia | REC |
| | Sarcosporidia (*Sarcocystidea*) | | REC |
| | | Sarcosporidia | REC |
| | | Globidia | REC |
| | Haplosporidia (*Aplosporidia*) | | REC |
| | | Haplosporidia | REC |

[7] *Includes:* Euplasmodida, Eumycetozoa, Sorophora, Acrasiae, Amaurochaetaceae, Amaurochaetineae, Amaurosporales, Anemineae, Arcyriaceae, Calcarineae, Calonemineae, Ceratiomyxaceae, Dictyosteliaceae, Didymiaceae, Endosporeae, Exosporae, Guttulinaceae, Heterodermaceae, Lamprosporales, Liceaceae, Lygogalaceae, Margaritaceae, Physaraceae, Reticulariaceae, Stemonitaceae, Trichiaceae, Tubulinaceae.

[8] *Includes:* Allogromidiaceae, Astrorhizidea, Cheilostomellaceae, Chilostomellidea, Globigerinidea, Gromiidea, Lagenidea, Lituolidea, Miliolidia, Nummulitidea, Rotalidea, Textularidea, Xenophyophoridea.

[9] *Includes:* Actinophrydea, Aphrothoraca, Centrohelidia, Chalarothoraca, Chlamydophora, Desmothoraca, Helioflagellida.

[10] *Includes:* Acantharia, Acanthometrida, Acanthophractida, Actipylaea, Cyrtellaria, Botryoidea, Cyrtoidea, Spyroidea, Monopylaria, Nasselaria, Osculosida, Merotrypasta, Peripylaria, Spumellaria, Collodaria, Sphaerellaria, Sphaerozoa, Plectellaria, Plectoidea, Stephoidea, Porulosida, Holotrypasta, Tripylaria, Phaeodaria, Phaeoconchia, Phaeocystina, Tripylaea, Phaeogromia, Phaeosphaeria).

[11] Neosporidea (Histosporidia, Endospora) = CNIDOSPORIDIA + SARCOSPORIDIA + HAPLOSPORIDIA. Acnidosporidia = SARCOSPORIDIA + HAPLOSPORIDIA.

| Class | Subcl | Order | | |
|---|---|---|---|---|

**CILIATA** JUR-REC

    Protociliata (*Ciliatoidea*) REC

        Opalinida REC

    Euciliata JUR-REC

        Holotricha [16] (*Aspirigera, Aspirotricha*) REC

        Spirotricha [17] (*Spirigera*) JUR-REC

        Chonotricha REC

        Peritricha REC

**SUCTORIA** (*Acineta, Acinetaria, Tentaculifera*) REC

    Suctoria REC

## PORIFERA [18]

**CALCAREA** [19] (*Calcispongea*) CAM-REC

    Solenida (*Asconosa*) CAM-REC

    Lebetida (*Syconosa*) JUR-REC

    Pharetronida PER-REC

    Thalamida (*Sphinctozoa*) PEN-CRE

**HYALOSPONGEA** [20] (*Hexactinellida, Triaxonida*) CAM-REC

    Lyssakina (*Lyssacina*) CAM-REC

    Dictyonina (*Dictyida, Inermia*) ORD-REC

    Lychniskophora (*Lychniskida*) JUR-REC

    Heteractinida CAM-CAR

**DEMOSPONGEA** [21] (*Desmospongea*) CAM-REC

    Myxospongida REC

    Keratosida [22] (*Ceratospongida, Ceratosa, Ceratosida,* CAR-REC
    Euceratosa*)

[12] *Includes:* Rhabdogeniae, Serosporidia, Exosporidia, Piroplasmidea.

[13] *Includes:* Eugregarinida, Schizogregarinida.

[14] *Includes:* Adeleida, Eimeriida.

[15] *Includes:* Babesiida, Plasmodiida.

[16] *Includes:* Apostomina, Aspirotrichaceae, Astomata, Astomina, Gymnostomata, Hymenostomata, Thigmotrichina, Trichostomata.

[17] *Includes:* Ctenostomina, Entodiniomorphina, Heterotricha, Hypotricha, Oligotrichina, Polytricha, Tintinnina.

[18] *Synonyms:* Spongiaria, Spongeae. *Includes:* Octactinellida, Heteractinellida. Silicospongiae (Non-calcarea) = HEXACTINELLIDA + DEMOSPONGEA. Nidulitida, sometimes included here, is probably a calcareous alga.

[19] Asconosa, Syconosa, Leuconosa are structural types, not groups. *Includes:* Sycones, Dialytina, Lithonina, Homocoelida, Heterocoelida.

[20] *Includes:* Hexasterophora, Amphidiscophora, Uncinataria.

[21] *Includes:* Tetractinellida, Tetraxonida, Desmophora, Monaxonida, Sigmatomonaxonellida, Monactinellida.

[22] Considered by some to belong to Hadromerida. Sometimes placed with some others of Demospongea as Cornacuspongia (with orders Protorhabdina, Poikilorhabdina, Phthinorhabdina, Aporhabdina). *Includes:* Dictyoceratina, Monoceratina, Dendroceratina, Hexaceratina.

| Class | Subcl | Order | |
|---|---|---|---|
| | | Haplosclerida | CAM-REC |
| | | Poecilosclerida | CAM-REC |
| | | Hadromerida (*Astromonaxonellida*) | CAM-REC |
| | | Halichondrida | REC |
| | | Epipolasida | CAM-REC |
| | | Choristida (*Astrophora, Sigmatophora*) | CAR-REC |
| | | Carnosida (*Homosclerophora, Microsclerophora*) | CAR-REC |
| | | Lithistida | CAM-REC |
| RECEPTACULITIDA [23] | | | ORD-DEV |
| | | Receptaculitida | ORD-DEV |

## CYATHOSPONGIA [24]

| | | | |
|---|---|---|---|
| MONOCYATHA | | | CAM |
| | | Monocyathida | CAM |
| | | Archaeophyllida | CAM |
| ARCHAEOCYATHA | | | CAM |
| | | Ajacicyathida | CAM |
| | | Metacyathida | CAM |
| | | Acanthinocyathida | CAM |
| | | Hetairacyathida | CAM |
| | | Syringocnemida | CAM |
| ANTHOCYATHA | | | CAM |
| | | Anthomorphida | CAM |
| | | Somphocyathida | CAM |

## MESOZOA [25]

| | | | |
|---|---|---|---|
| RHOMBOZOA | | | REC |
| | | Dicyemida | REC |
| | | Heterocyemida | REC |
| ORTHONECTIDA | | | REC |
| | | Orthonectida | REC |

## MONOBLASTOZOA

| | | | |
|---|---|---|---|
| MONOBLASTOIDEA | | | REC |
| | | Monoblastidea | REC |

[23] *Affinities unknown; may not belong to Porifera.*

[24] *Includes:* Acanthocyatha, Uranocyatha, Exocyatha. *Synonyms:* Pleospongia.

[25] *Synonyms:* Planuloidea, Mionelminthes, Moruloidea. Catenata are now considered to be parasitic dinoflagellates (Protozoa).

[26] *Includes:* Rhabdophora, Retioloidea. Acanthaspida, Acanthistida, Graptoblasti, Graptovermida are groups of uncertain status.

# GRAPTOZOA[26]

| | | |
|---|---|---|
| GRAPTOLITHIDA | | CAM-MIS |
| | Dendroidea | CAM-MIS |
| | Graptoloidea | ORD-SIL |
| | Tuboidea | ORD-SIL |
| | Camaroidea | ORD |
| | Stolonoidea | ORD |

# CONULARIDA

| | | |
|---|---|---|
| CONULATA | | CAM-TRI |
| | Conulariida | CAM-TRI |

# COELENTERATA[27]

| | | |
|---|---|---|
| PROTOMEDUSAE | | CAM-ORD |
| | Brooksellida | CAM-ORD |
| DIPLEUROZOA | | CAM |
| | Dickinsoniida | CAM |
| STROMATOPOROIDEA | | CAM-CRE |
| | Stromatoporidea | CAM-CRE |
| | Labechioidea | ORD-CRE |
| | Sphaeractinoidea | JUR-CRE |
| HYDROZOA [28] (*Anoecia, Ectocarpen, Aphacellae, Hydrozoaria*) | | CAM-REC |
| | Trachylinida [29] | JUR-REC |
| | Hydroida [30] (*Nudibrachiata, Polypiaria, Hydrida, Hydrariae, Diplomorpha*) | CAM-REC |
| | Spongiomorphida | TRI-JUR |
| | Milleporida (*Hydrocorallinae*) | CRE-REC |
| | Stylasterina | CRE-REC |
| | Siphonophora [31] | ORD-REC |

[27] *Synonyms:* Cnidaria, Nematozoa, Nematophora.

[28] *Includes:* Eleutheroblastea, Hydromedusae.

[29] *Includes:* Trachymedusae, Trachomedusae, Narcomedusae.

[30] *Includes:* Anthomedusae, Athecata, Gymnoblastea, Leptomedusae, Thecata, Thecaphora, Calyptoblastea, Leptolinae, Sertularina, Campanulariae, Tubulariae.

[31] *Includes:* Calycophora, Physophora, Chondrophora.

Class   Subcl   Order

SCYPHOZOA [32] (*Scyphomedusae, Acalephae, Neoscyphozoa,*    JUR-REC
   *Acraspeda*)

   Stauromedusae (*Lucernaria, Lucernariidea, Cyclico-*    REC
   *zoa, Calycozoa*)

   Cubomedusae (*Carybdeida, Charybdeida, Marsupi-* JUR-REC
   *alia*)

   Coronatae (*Peromedusae, Corona, Coronatida*)    JUR-REC

   Semaeostomeae (*Semostomeae, Semaeostomatida*)    JUR-REC

   Lithorhizostomeae (*Lithorhizostomatida*)    JUR

   Rhizostomeae (Rhizostomatida)    JUR-REC

ANTHOZOA (*Endoaria, Actinozoa, Actinoidea, Oecioa, Polycy-* CAM-REC
   *clia, Corallaria, Monocyclica, Coralligena, Coralla,*
   *Scyphopolypi, Anthozoariae*)

   Alcyonaria [33] (*Octocorallia, Octactinia, Zoophytaria*)    PER-REC

   Stolonifera    CRE-REC

   Telestacea    REC

   Alcyonacea    JUR-REC

   Trachypsammiacea    PER

   Coenothecalia    CRE-REC

   Gorgonacea    CRE-REC

   Pennatulacea    CRE-REC

   Zoantharia [34] (*Hexacorallia, Helianthoida, Zoanthactiniaria,* CAM-REC
   *Actinanthida, Dodecacorallia, Zoantha*)

   Zoanthiniaria (*Zoanthidea*)    REC

   Corallimorpharia (*Stichodactylina, Asclerocorallia*)    REC

   Actiniaria (*Actiniidea, Malacactiniae, Edwardsiidea*) CAM-REC

   Rugosa (*Stauracea, Pterocorallia, Tetraseptata, Tetra-* ORD-PER
   *coelia, Tetracorallia*)

   Heterocorallia (*Dicoelia*)    CAR

   Scleractinia (*Madreporaria, Polyactinia, Cyclocoral-* TRI-REC
   *lia*)

   Tabulata (*Aseptata, Trichocorallia, Tubulosa, Tetra-* ORD-PER
   *dida, Schizocoralla, Heliolitida, Multisolenida, Thal-*
   *locoralla, Chaetetida*)

[32] Discomedusae (Discophora) = CORONATAE + SEMAEOSTOMEAE + RHIZO-
STOMEAE.

[33] *Includes:* Pseudaxonia, Axifera, Stelechotokea, Protalcyonacea, Synalcyonacea.

[34] *Includes:* Paramera, Cryptoparamera, Ptychodactiaria, Proactiniae.

[35] *Synonyms:* Acnidaria, Collaria, Ctenophoraria, Ctenarea.

[36] *Synonyms:* Platodes, Platyelmia, Plathelminthes, Platyhelmia. Cestoidea =
CESTODA + CESTODARIA.

Ceriantipatharia    MIO-REC

    Antipatharia (*Hexactinia, Anticorallia, Antipathidea*)   MIO-REC

    Ceriantharia (*Paranemata, Tetractiniae, Heterocoralla, Cerianthiae, Cerianthidea*)   REC

## CTENOPHORA [35]

TENTACULATA (*Micropharyngea*)    REC

    Cydippida (*Saccata*)    REC

    Lobata (*Bolinopsidea*)    REC

    Cestida (*Cestoidea*)    REC

    Platyctenea (*Tjalfiellidea, Ctenoplanidea*)    REC

NUDA (*Macropharyngea, Atentaculata*)    REC

    Beroida    REC

## PLATYHELMINTHES [36]

TURBELLARIA (*Planaria*)    REC

    Acoela    REC

    Rhabdocoela [37]    REC

    Alloeocoela (*Alloiocoela*)    REC

    Tricladida    REC

    Polycladida (*Cryptocoela*)    REC

TREMATODA    REC

    Monogenea [38] (*Monogenetica, Heterocotylea, Eterocotylea, Herocotylida, Polystomea, Pectobothrii, Cryptocoela, Ectoparasitica*)    REC

    Aspidogastrea (*Aspidobothria, Aspidocotylea*)    REC

    Digenea [39] (*Digenetica, Malacocotylea, Distomea, Malacobothrii, Strigeata*)    REC

CESTODA [40] (*Eucestoda, Cestoidea, Merozoa, Polyzoa, Tomiosoma*)    REC

    Proteocephala (*Proteocephaloidea*)    REC

    Tetraphyllidea (*Phyllobothrioidea*)    REC

    Disculicepitidea    REC

    Lecanicephala (*Lecanicephaloidea, Diphyllidea*)    REC

[37] *Includes:* Temnocephaloidea, Dactylifera, Catenulida, Macrostomida.

[38] *Includes:* Monopisthocotylea, Polyopisthocotylea.

[39] *Includes:* Gasterostoma, Prosostomata.

[40] *Includes:* Aphylles, Monophyllidea, Heterophyllidea, Cystica, Caryophyllacea.

| Class | Subcl | Order | |
|---|---|---|---|
| | | Trypanorhyncha (*Tetrarhyncha, Tetrarhynchoidea, Phyllorhyncha*) | REC |
| | | Cyclophyllidea (*Taenioidea, Tetracotylea, Tetrabothridiata*) | REC |
| | | Aporidea | REC |
| | | Nippotaeniidea | REC |
| | | Caryophyllidea | REC |
| | | Spathebothridea | REC |
| | | Pseudophyllidea (*Bothriocephaloidea, Dicestoda, Dibothridiata*) | REC |
| CESTODARIA (*Monozoa, Atomiosoma*) | | | REC |
| | | Amphilinidea | REC |
| | | Gyrocotylidea | REC |
| | | Biporophyllidea | REC |

## RHYNCHOCOELA [41]

| | | | |
|---|---|---|---|
| NEMERTINEA [42] (*Nemertea*) | | | REC |
| | | Palaeonemertea (*Paleonemertea, Palaeonemertini*) | REC |
| | | Heteronemertea (*Schizonemertini, Trimyaria, Eupolida*) | REC |
| | | Hoplonemertea (*Metanemertini*) | REC |
| | | Bdellonemertea (*Bdellomorpha*) | REC |

## ACANTHOCEPHALA

| | | | |
|---|---|---|---|
| ACANTHOCEPHALA [43] | | | REC |
| | | Archiacanthocephala | REC |
| | | Palaeacanthocephala | REC |
| | | Eoacanthocephala [44] | REC |

## ROTIFERA [45]

| | | | |
|---|---|---|---|
| SEISONIDEA | | | REC |
| | | Seisonacea | REC |
| BDELLOIDEA | | | REC |
| | | Bdellacea (*Bdelloidaceae*) | REC |

[41] *Synonyms:* Aplocoela, Miocoela.
[42] *Includes:* Dimyaria, Protonemertini, Mesonemertini, Anopla, Enopla.
[43] Metacanthocephala = ARCHIACANTHOCEPHALA + PALAEACANTHOCEPHALA
[44] *Includes:* Gyracanthocephala, Neoacanthocephala.
[45] *Synonyms:* Rotatoria. Digononta = SEISONIDEA + BDELLOIDEA.
[46] *Includes:* Rhizota.

| Class | Subcl | Order | |
|-------|-------|-------|---|
| **MONOGONONTA** [46] | | | REC |
| | Ploima [47] (*Ploimoidaceae*) | | REC |
| | Flosculariacea [48] | | REC |
| | Collothecacea | | REC |

## GASTROTRICHA

| | | REC |
|---|---|---|
| **MACRODASYOIDEA** | | REC |
| | Macrodasyidea | REC |
| **CHAETONOTOIDEA** | | REC |
| | Chaetonotidea | REC |

## KINORHYNCHA

| | | REC |
|---|---|---|
| **ECHINODERA** | | REC |
| | Echinodera [49] | REC |

## PRIAPULOIDEA

| | | REC |
|---|---|---|
| **PRIAPULOIDEA** | | REC |
| | Priapulida | REC |

## NEMATODA [50]

| | | REC |
|---|---|---|
| **NEMATOIDEA** | | REC |
| | Enoploidea (*Enoplata*) | REC |
| | Dorylaimoidea | REC |
| | Mermithoidea | REC |
| | Chromadoroidea [51] | REC |
| | Araeolaimoidea | REC |
| | Monhysteroidea | REC |
| | Desmoscolecoidea | REC |
| | Rhabditoidea (*Anguilluloidea*) | REC |
| | Rhabdiasoidea | REC |

[47] *Includes:* Notommatoidea, Brachionoidea, Asplanchnaceae, Loricata, Illoricata.

[48] *Includes:* Scirtopoda, Trochosphaerida, Melicertida.

[49] *Includes:* Cyclorhaga, Conchorhaga, Homalorhaga, as suborders.

[50] *Synonym:* Nemata. *Includes:* Hologonia, Telogonia, Phasmidia, Aphasmidia.

[51] *Includes:* Chaetosomatida.

| Class | Subcl | Order | |
|-------|-------|-------|---|
| | | Oxyuroidea | REC |
| | | Ascaroidea | REC |
| | | Strongyloidea | REC |
| | | Spiruroidea (*Camallanta*) | REC |
| | | Dracunculoidea | REC |
| | | Filarioidea | REC |
| | | Trichuroidea (*Trichinelloidea*) | REC |
| | | Dioctophymoidea | REC |

## GORDIACEA

| | | | |
|-------|-------|-------|---|
| NEMATOMORPHA | | | CAR-REC |
| | | Gordioidea (*Gordididea*) | CAR-REC |
| | | Nectonematoidea | REC |

## CALYSSOZOA [52]

| | | | |
|-------|-------|-------|---|
| ENDOPROCTA (*Entoprocta*) | | | REC |
| | | Pedicellinida | REC |

## BRYOZOA [53]

| | | | |
|-------|-------|-------|---|
| PHYLACTOLAEMATA (*Hippocrepia*) | | | CRE-REC |
| | | Lophopoda | CRE-REC |
| GYMNOLAEMATA [54] (*Stelmatopoda*) | | | ORD-REC |
| | | Trepostomata (*Tripostomata, Monticuliporoidea*) | ORD-PER |
| | | Cryptostomata | ORD-PER |
| | | Cyclostomata (*Stenostomata*) | ORD-REC |
| | | Ctenostomata | ORD-REC |
| | | Cheilostomata (*Chilostomata*) | CRE-REC |

## PHORONIDA

| | | | |
|-------|-------|-------|---|
| PHORONIDA | | | REC |
| | | Phoronida | REC |

[52] *Synonyms:* Kamptozoa (see also class names).

[53] *Synonyms:* Polyzoa, Ectoprocta. Formerly included also Endoprocta; together called also Holobranchia.

[54] Stenolaemata = TREPOSTOMATA + CYCLOSTOMATA. Cheiloctenostoma (Eurystomata) = CTENOSTOMATA + CHEILOSTOMATA.

[55] *Synonyms:* Spirobranchiopoda, Palliobranchiopoda, Branchiopoda, Brachionopoda, Brachionocephala, Branchionobranchia, Spirobranchia.

[56] *Includes:* Orthida, Strophomenida.

[57] *Includes:* Pentamerida, Rhynchonellida, Spiriferida, Terebratulida, Triplesiida.

[58] *Synonyms:* Palliata, Malacozoa, Heterogangliata, Otocardia, Saccata. Glossophora (Cephalophora) = AMPHINEURA + GASTROPODA + CEPHALOPODA + SCA-

# BRACHIOPODA [55]

INARTICULATA (*Ecardines, Lyopomata, Pleuropygia, Gastrocau-* CAM-REC
 *lia, Tretenterata, Sarcobranchiata*)
  Atremata                                                   CAM-REC
  Neotremata                                                 CAM-REC
ARTICULATA (*Testicardines, Arthropomata, Apygia, Pygocaulia,* CAM-REC
 *Clistenterata*)
  Palaeotremata (*Paleotremata*)                             CAM
  Protremata [56]                                            CAM-REC
  Telotremata [57]                                           CAM-REC

# MOLLUSCA [58]

MONOPLACOPHORA [59] (*Protogastropoda, Amphigastropoda*)     CAM-REC
  Tryblidioidea (*Tryblidiacea*)                             CAM-REC
  Archinacelloidea                                           CAM-SIL
  Cambridioidea                                              CAM
AMPHINEURA [60] (*Aculifera, Polyplacophora, Loricata, Crepi-* CAM-REC
 *poda, Polyplakiphora, Polyplaxiphora, Placophora,*
 *Polybranchiata, Lamellata, Lepidoglossa*)
  Paleoloricata                                              CAM-CRE
  Neoloricata                                                CAR-REC
APLACOPHORA (*Solenogastres, Telobranchia, Scolecomorpha*)   REC
  Neomeniida (*Neomeniomorpha*)                              REC
  Chaetodermatida (*Chaetodermomorpha*)                      REC
GASTROPODA [61] (*Anisopleura, Paracephalophora, Pselapho-*  CAM-REC
 *cephala*)
  Prosobranchia (*Streptoneura, Cochlides*)                  CAM-REC
  Archaeogastropoda [62]                                     CAM-REC

PHOPODA. Stenolaemata = AMPHINEURA + GASTROPODA + BIVALVIA + SCAPHOPODA.
Prorhipidoglossomorpha = GASTROPODA + BIVALVIA + SCAPHOPODA. Isopleura =
MONOPLACOPHORA + AMPHINEURA + APLACOPHORA.

   [59] *Includes:* Cynostraca, Cochliostraca.

   [60] *Includes:* Lepidopleurida, Chitonida, Eoplacophora, Isoplacophora, Mesoplacophora, Teleoplacophora.

   [61] *Also spelled:* Gasteropoda, Gastraeopoda, Gasteropodophora, Gasterozoa.
*Includes:* Spironotia. Euthyneura (Androgyna, Platymalakia) = OPISTHOBRANCHIA
+ PULMONATA.

   [62] *Includes:* Scutibranchia, Aspidobranchiata, Diotocardia, Bellerophontacea,
Cyclobranchia, Zygobranchia, Docoglossa, Rhipidoglossa.

| Class | Subcl | Order | |
|---|---|---|---|
| | | Caenogastropoda [63] | ORD-REC |
| | Opisthobranchia [64] | | MIS-REC |
| | | Pleurocoela [65] (*Tectibranchiata, Tectobranchia, Aply-* | MIS-REC |
| | | *siacea, Steganobranchia*) | |
| | | Pteropoda | CRE-REC |
| | | Sacoglossa | REC |
| | | Acoela [66] | EOC-REC |
| | Pulmonata | | PEN-REC |
| | | Basommatophora | PEN-REC |
| | | Stylommatophora | PEN-REC |
| BIVALVIA [67] (*Pelecypoda, Lamellibranchiata, Aglossa, Lipoce-* | | | ORD-REC |
| *phala, Conchifera, Conchophora, Acephala*) | | | |
| | | Protobranchia [68] | ORD-REC |
| | | Filibranchia [69] | ORD-REC |
| | | Eulamellibranchia [70] | SIL-REC |
| | | Septibranchia | JUR-REC |
| SCAPHOPODA (*Cirrhobranchiata, Solenoconchia, Prosopocepha-* | | | DEV-REC |
| *la, Lateribranchiata*) | | | |
| | | Scaphopoda | DEV-REC |
| CEPHALOPODA (*Siphonopoda*) | | | CAM-REC |
| | Tetrabranchiata (*Schizosiphona, Tentaculifera*) | | CAM-REC |
| | | Nautiloidea [71] | CAM-REC |
| | | Ammonitoidea [72] | ORD-CRE |
| | Dibranchiata (*Coleoidea, Acetabulifera, Holosiphona*) | | MIS-REC |
| | | Decapoda [73] (*Decembrachiata, Decabrachia*) | JUR-REC |

[63] *Includes:* Siphonobranchia, Pectinibranchia, Ctenobranchiata, Hemipomatostoma, Apomatostoma, Monotocardia, Azygobranchia, Mesogastropoda, Stenoglossa, Neogastropoda, Rachiglossa, Toxoglossa, Heteropoda, Taenioglossa, Platypoda, Rhachiglossa.

[64] *Includes:* Gymnosomata, Oncidiacea, Acochlidiacea, Vaginulacea, Anaspidea.

[65] *Includes:* Cephalaspidea, Thecosomata, Bullomorpha, Gyrosomata.

[66] *Includes:* Notaspidea, Pleurobranchomorpha, Nudibranchiata.

[67] *Includes:* Anisomyaria, Anatinacea, Cladocopa, Ambonodonta. Groups sometimes recognized include: Siphonida, Asiphonida, Homomyaria, Macrociliobranchia, Microciliobranchia, Pteriomorpha, Colloconchida, Eutaxodonta, Isofilibranchia, Pteroconchida, Rostroconchida, Heteroconchia, Eudesmodontida, Naiadida, Pachyodontida, Pantodontida, Asthenodontida, Schizodontida, Heterodontida, Septibranchida. Also used as orders: Autobranchiata, Dimyaria, Eleutherorhabda, Hemibranchia, Heteromya, Heteromyaria, Isedrolotila, Isomya, Laternulacea, Macrotrachia, Monomyaria, Monomya, Neotaxodonta, Palaeobranchia, Palaeolamellibranchia, Parafilibranchia, Pholadacea, Pleuroconcha, Pleurodonta, Praeheterodonta, Synaptorhabda, Veneracea.

**Class   Subcl   Order**

Octopoda (*Octobrachiata, Octopoida*)          CRE-REC
Vampyromorpha                                              REC
Belemnoida [74] (*Phragmophora*)              MIS-EOC

## SIPUNCULOIDEA

SIPUNCULOIDEA                                              REC
Sipunculida                                              REC

## ECHIUROIDEA

ECHIURIDA                                                    REC
Echiuroina                                              REC
Xenopneusta                                              REC
Heteromyota                                              REC
SACCOSOMATIDA                                              REC
Saccosomatida                                              REC

## MYZOSTOMIDA [75]

MYZOSTOMIDA                                              PAL-REC
Proboscidea                                              REC
Pharyngidea                                              REC

Arrangement preferred by paleontologists:
Subclass Prionodesmacea (orders Paleoconcha, Taxodonta, Schizodonta, Isodonta, Dysodonta).
Subclass Anomalodesmacea (orders Septibranchia, Anomalobranchia).
Subclass Teleodesmacea (orders Pantodonta, Diogenodonta, Cyclodonta, Teleodonta, Asthenodonta, Heterodonta, Pachyodonta, Desmodonta)

[68] Sometimes a subclass with orders Cryptodonta, Lipodonta, Palaeotaxodonta.
[69] *Includes:* Pseudolamellibranchia.
[70] *Includes:* Schizodonta, Heterodonta, Adapedonta, Anomalodesmata, Sinupalliata, Integripalliata.
[71] Sometimes ranked as a separate subclass with orders Mixochoanites, Schistochoanites, Orthochoanites, Cyrtochoanites; or with orders Ellesmeroceroida, Michelinoceroida, Ascoceroida, Oncoceroida, Endoceroida, Actinoceroida, Discosoroida, Nautilida; or with orders Bassleroceratida, Barrandeoceratida, Centroceratida, Rutoceratida, Solenochilida, Tarphyceratida.
[72] Sometimes ranked as a separate subclass with order Ammonitida; or with orders Intrasiphonata, Extrasiphonata.
[73] *Includes:* Teuthoidea, Sepioidea, Loliginacea, Architeuthacea.
[74] Sometimes used as subclass in place of Dibranchiata.
[75] *Synonyms:* Myzostomaria, Myzostoma.

Class    Subcl    Order

# ANNELIDA [76]

| | |
|---|---|
| CHAETOPODA [77] | CAM-REC |
|   Polychaeta [78] | CAM-REC |
|     Errantia (*Phanerocephala*) | CEN-REC |
|     Sedentaria (*Cryptocephala, Tubicola*) | ORD-REC |
|     Miskoa | CAM |
|   Oligochaeta [79] | ORD-REC |
|     Plesiothecata | ?-REC |
|     Prosothecata | ?-REC |
|     Prosopora | ?-REC |
|     Opisthopora | ?-REC |
| HIRUDINEA | REC |
|     Rhynchobdellida (*Rhynchobdelliformes*) | REC |
|     Gnathobdellida (*Gnathobdelliformes*) | REC |
|     Pharyngobdellida (*Herpobdellida, Erpobdellida, Pharyngobdelliformes*) | REC |
|     Acanthobdellida (*Acanthobdelliformes*) | REC |
| ARCHIANNELIDA [80] | REC |
|     Archiannelida | REC |

# TARDIGRADA

| | |
|---|---|
| HETEROTARDIGRADA | REC |
|     Arthrotardigrada (*Prototardigrada*) | REC |
|     Echiniscoidea | REC |
| EUTARDIGRADA | REC |
|     Eutardigrada | REC |

[76] *Synonyms:* Annulata, Coelhelminthes. Clitellata = OLIGOCHAETA + HIRUDINEA.

[77] *Includes:* Haplodrili, Saccocirrida.

[78] *Includes:* Nereidiformia, Capitelliformia, Spioniformia, Terebelliformia, Scoleciformia, Archichaetopoda, Poeobioidea.

[79] *Includes:* Aphaneura, Limicolae, Moniligastres, Terricolae, Naidomorpha, Lumbricimorpha. Plesiothecata and Prosothecata have previously been cited as Plesiopora plesiotheca and Plesiopora prosotheca.

[80] *Includes:* Dinophilea.

[81] *Synonyms:* Polypoda, Protracheata, Ceratophora, Malacopoda.

[82] *Synonyms:* Euarthropoda. *Subphyla:* Trilobitomorpha (Anomomeristica) = TRILOBITOIDEA + TRILOBITA; Chelicerata (Nomomeristica) = MEROSTOMATA + PYCNOGONIDA + ARACHNIDA; Mandibulata = CRUSTACEA + PAUROPODA + SYM-

Class    Subcl    Order

## PENTASTOMIDA

LINGUATULIDA                                                                    REC
    Cephalobaenida                                                         REC
    Porocephalida (*Linguatulodea*)                                        REC

## ONYCHOPHORA [81]

PERIPATIDEA                                                                CAM-REC
    Protonychophora                                                        CAM
    Euonychophora                                                          REC

## ARTHROPODA [82]

TRILOBITOIDEA [83]                                                         CAM-PEN
    Merostomoidea (*Xenopoda*)                                             CAM
      Limulavida (*Prochelicerata, Limulava*)                           CAM
      Emeraldellida                                                     CAM
      Nectaspida                                                        CAM
      Leanchoiliida (*Pseudanostraca*)                                  CAM
    Pseudonotostraca (*Pseudocrustacea*)                                   CAM
      Burgessiida                                                       CAM
      Waptiida                                                          CAM
    Marrellomorpha [84] (*Marellomorpha*)                                  CAM
      Marrellida                                                        CAM
    Hymenocarina                                                           CAM
      Hymenocarina                                                      CAM
    Arthropleurida                                                         PEN
      Arthropleurida                                                    PEN
    Cheloniellida                                                          DEV
      Cheloniellida                                                     DEV
    Opabiniida                                                             CAM
      Palaeanostraca                                                    CAM

PHYLA + DIPLOPODA + CHILOPODA + INSECTA. Hyparthropoda was proposed for hypothetical ancestral forms. A separate class Arthrocephala is listed by Boettger in the Chelicerata, but no other reference to such an extinct group has been found. Diantennata = TRILOBITOMORPHA + CRUSTACEA. Branchiata = TRILOBITOMORPHA + CHELICERATA + MANDIBULATA. Acerata = MEROSTOMATA + ARACHNIDA. Arachnomorpha = TRILOBITOMORPHA + CRUSTACEA. Myriapoda = PAUROPODA + SYMPHYLA + DIPLOPODA + CHILOPODA. Progoneata = SYMPHYLA + DIPLOPODA + PAUROPODA. Antennata = PAUROPODA + SYMPHYLA + DIPLOPODA + CHILOPODA + INSECTA. Opisthogoneata = CHILOPODA + INSECTA. *Includes:* Marriocarida, of unknown position.

[83] Homopoda = MARRELLINA + PSEUDANOSTRACA + PSEUDONOTOSTRACA + HYMENOCARINA.

[84] *Includes:* Mimetasterida, Pygaspida, Proarthropoda.

| Class | Subcl | Order | |
|---|---|---|---|
| TRILOBITA [85] | | | CAM-PER |
| | | Agnostida (*Isopygia, Miomera*) | CAM-ORD |
| | | Redlichiida (*Micropygia, Mesonacida*) | CAM |
| | | Corynexochida (*Bathyuriscidea, Zacanthoidacea*) | CAM |
| | | Ptychopariida (*Conocoryphida, Trinucleida*) | CAM-PER |
| | | Phacopida (*Proparia*) | ORD-DEV |
| | | Lichida (*Lichacea*) | ORD-DEV |
| | | Odontopleurida | CAM-DEV |
| MEROSTOMATA [86] (*Palaeostraca*) | | | CAM-REC |
| | Xiphosura (*Gnathopoda, Poecilopoda*) | | CAM-REC |
| | | Aglaspida | CAM-ORD |
| | | Xiphosurida [87] | SIL-REC |
| | Eurypterida | | ORD-PER |
| | | Gigantostraca | ORD-PER |
| PYCNOGONIDA (*Pantopoda*) | | | DEV-REC |
| | | Eupantopoda [88] | REC |
| | | Palaeopantopoda | DEV |
| ARACHNIDA [89] (*Embolobranchiata, Aeropneusta, Eu-arach-nida*) | | | SIL-REC |
| | Latigastra | | SIL-REC |
| | | Scorpionida (*Scorpiones, Pectinifera*) | SIL-REC |
| | | Pseudoscorpionida (*Chelonethida, Chernetes, Chernetidea*) | OLI-REC |
| | | Phalangida (*Opiliones, Opilionidea*) | PEN-REC |
| | | Architarbida (*Architarbi, Phalangiotarbi*) | CAR |
| | | Acarida [90] (*Acari, Acarina, Rhynchostomi, Monomerostomata*) | DEV-REC |
| | Stethostomata | | CAR |
| | | Haptopodida (*Haptopoda*) | CAR |
| | | Anthracomartida (*Anthracomarti*) | CAR |
| | Soluta | | DEV-CAR |
| | | Trigonotarbida (*Trigonotarbi*) | DEV-CAR |
| | Caulogastra [91, 92] | | CAR-REC |

[85] *Includes:* Opisthoparia, Hypoparia, Integricephalida, Oligomeria, Pliomeria, Protoparia, Epiparia, Polymera, Eodiscida, Olenellida.

[86] Delobranchia (Hydropneustea) = MEROSTOMATA (sometimes + TRILOBITOMORPHA).

[87] *Includes:* Synxiphosurida, Bunodomorpha, Limulida, Euxiphosura.

[88] *Includes:* Colossendeomorpha, Nymphonomorpha, Ascorhynchomorpha, Pycnogonomorpha.

[89] Epectinata = all ARACHNIDA except SCORPIONIDA. Arachnoidea = class ARACHNIDA or ARACHNIDA + MEROSTOMATA.

| Class | Subcl | Order | |
|---|---|---|---|
| | | Palpigradida (*Microthelyphonida, Latisterna, Palpigradi*) | JUR-REC |
| | | Thelyphonida (*Uropygi, Holopeltidia*) | CAR-REC |
| | | Schizomida (*Tartarides, Schizopeltidia, Colopyga, Schizonotida*) | PLI-REC |
| | | Kustarachnida (*Kustarachne*) | PEN |
| | | Phrynichida (*Amblypygi, Phryneides*) | CAR-REC |
| | | Araneida (*Araneae*) | CAR-REC |
| | | Solpugida (*Solifugae, Galeodea, Rostrata, Mycetophorae*) | CAR-REC |
| | | Ricinuleida (*Rhinogastra, Meridogastra, Podogonata, Cucullifera, Rhignogastra*) | CAR-REC |
| CRUSTACEA [93] (*Eucrustacea*) | | | CAM-REC |
| | Branchiopoda [94] | | CAM-REC |
| | | Anostraca (*Euanostraca*) | EOC-REC |
| | | Lipostraca | DEV |
| | | Notostraca | PER-REC |
| | | Conchostraca | DEV-REC |
| | | Cladocera | REC |
| | Cephalocarida | | REC |
| | | Cephalocarida | REC |
| | Ostracoda (*Ostracopa, Ostrapoda*) | | CAM-REC |
| | | Archaeocopida [95] (*Archaeostraca*) | CAM-TRI |
| | | Leperditicopida (*Leperditiida*) | ORD-DEV |
| | | Myodocopida (*Myodocopa, Cladocopa*) | ORD-REC |
| | | Podocopida (*Podocopa, Platycopa*) | ORD-REC |
| | | Palaeocopida (*Paleocopa, Beyrichiida*) | ORD-PER |
| | Mystacocarida | | REC |
| | | Mystacocarida | REC |
| | Copepoda (*Eucopepoda*) | | REC |
| | | Calanoida | REC |
| | | Harpacticoida | REC |
| | | Cyclopoida | REC |

[90] *Includes:* Notostigmata, Cryptostigmata, Prostigmata, Stomatostigmata, Heterostigmata, Parastigmata, Mesostigmata, Metastigmata.

[91] Camarostomata = SCHIZOMIDA + THELYPHONIDA + KUSTARACHNIDA. Labellata = PHRYNICHIDA + ARANEIDA.

[92] Pedipalpida (scorpion-spiders) = SCHIZOMIDA + THELYPHONIDA + PHRYNICHIDA.

[93] Entomostraca = BRANCHIOPODA + OSTRACODA + COPEPODA + CIRRIPEDIA.

[94] Diplostraca = CONCHOSTRACA + CLADOCERA. Phyllopoda (Euphyllopoda, Onychura) = ANOSTRACA + NOTOSTRACA + CONCHOSTRACA.

[95] *Includes:* Bradorina, Discinocarina.

| Class | Subcl | Order | |
|---|---|---|---|
| | | Notodelphyoida | REC |
| | | Monstrilloida | REC |
| | | Caligoida | REC |
| | | Lernaeopodoida | REC |
| | Branchiura | | REC |
| | | Branchiura | REC |
| | Cirripedia (*Thyrostraca, Eucirripedia*) | | SIL-REC |
| | | Thoracica | SIL-REC |
| | | Acrothoracica | REC |
| | | Ascothoracica | REC |
| | | Apoda | REC |
| | | Rhizocephala | REC |
| Malacostraca [96] | | | PER-REC |
| | | Nebaliacea | REC |
| | | Rhinocarina | DEV-PEN |
| | | Ceratiocarina (*Ceratocarina*) | CAM-PEN |
| | | Nahecarida | DEV |
| | | Anaspidacea (*Anomostraca, Syncarida*) | PEN-REC |
| | | Mysidacea [97] | MIS-REC |
| | | Thermosbaenacea | REC |
| | | Spelaeogriphacea | REC |
| | | Lophogastridea | REC |
| | | Cumacea (*Sympoda*) | REC |
| | | Tanaidacea (*Chelifera, Anisopoda*) | REC |
| | | Isopoda | DEV-REC |
| | | Amphipoda (*Laemodipoda*) | TER-REC |
| | | Euphausiacea | REC |
| | | Pygocephalomorpha | PAL |
| | | Decapoda [98] | TRI-REC |
| | | Stomatopoda (*Hoplocarida*) | MIS-REC |
| PAUROPODA | | | REC |
| | | Heterognatha | REC |

[96] Phyllocarida (Leptostraca) = NEBALIACEA + RHINOCARINA + CERATIOCARINA + HYMENOCARINA. Eumalacostraca = ANASPIDACEA + MYSIDACEA + THERMOSBAENACEA + CUMACEA + TANAIDACEA + ISOPODA + AMPHIPODA + EUPHAUSIACEA + DECAPODA + STOMATOPODA. Peracarida (Podophthalma, Thoracostraca, Schizopoda, Anaspides) = MYSIDACEA + THERMOSBAENACEA + LOPHOGASTRIDEA + CUMACEA + TANAIDACEA + ISOPODA + AMPHIPODA. Edriophthalma (Arthrostraca, Tetradecapoda) = ISOPODA + AMPHIPODA. Eucarida = EUPHAUSIACEA + DECAPODA + STOMATOPODA.

[97] Lophogastridea has sometimes been included here.

[98] *Includes:* Macrura, Anomura, Brachyura.

| Class | Subcl | Order | |
|---|---|---|---|

SYMPHYLA — REC
  Cephalostigmata — REC
DIPLOPODA [99] — PEN-REC
  Pselaphognatha (*Penicillata*) — REC
    Ancyrotricha — REC
    Lophotricha — REC
  Chilognatha [100] — TER-REC
    Limacomorpha — REC
    Oniscomorpha (*Armadillomorpha*) — TER-REC
    Ascospermophora — REC
    Colobognatha (*Platydesmiformia*) — TER-REC
    Nematophora (*Merochaeta*) — TER-REC
    Proterospermophora — REC
    Opisthospermophora — REC
  Protosyngnatha — PEN
    Protosyngnatha — PEN
  Archipolypoda — DEV-CAR
    Palaeocoxopleura (*Macrosterni*) — DEV-CAR
CHILOPODA (*Syngnatha*) — TER-REC
  Pleurostigmophora [101] (*Pleurostigma*) — TER-REC
    Geophilomorpha (*Geophylomorpha*) — TER-REC
    Scolopendromorpha — TER-REC
    Lithobiomorpha — TER-REC
    Craterostigma — REC
  Notostigmophora (*Notostigma*) — TER-REC
    Scutigeromorpha — TER-REC
INSECTA [102] (*Hexapoda*) — DEV-REC
  Apterygota (*Synaptera, Apterygogenea, Aptera*) — DEV-REC
    Protura (*Myrientomata, Mirientomata, Prothysanura, Panprotura, Ellipura, Anamerentoma*) — REC
    Thysanura (*Ectotrophi, Ectognatha*) — TRI-REC
    Entotrophi (*Entognatha, Diplura, Campodeoidea, Homerentoma, Panthysanura, Dicellura*) — MIO-REC

[99] *Includes:* Eurysterna, Paleomorpha.

[100] *Includes:* Opisthandria, Proterandria, Eugnatha, Polydesmoidea, Juliformia.

[101] Anamorpha = CRATEROSTIGMA + LITHOBIOMORPHA. Epimorpha = GEOPHIL-OMORPHA + SCOLOPENDROMORPHA.

[102] Includes extinct orders: Sypharopteroidea, Archodonata, Perielytrodea, Protephemerida, Eubleptidodea, Syntonopteroidea, Permoneurodia. Pterygota (Pterygogenea) = EXOPTERYGOTA + ENDOPTERYGOTA. Palaeoptera = PALAEO-DICTYOPTERA + MEGASECOPTERA + PROTOHEMIPTERA + PROTODONATA + ODONATA + EPHEMERIDA. Neoptera = EXOPTERYGOTA (except PALAEOPTERA) + ENDOPTERY-GOTA. Euentomata = DIPLURA + ECTOTROPHI + PTERYGOTA.

| Class | Subcl | Order | |
|---|---|---|---|
| | | Collembola (*Oligoentomata*) | DEV-REC |
| | Exopterygota [103] (*Heterometabola*) | | DEV-REC |
| | | Palaeodictyoptera [104] (*Eopaleodictyoptera*) | PEN-PER |
| | | Megasecoptera [105] (*Megasecopterida*) | PEN-PER |
| | | Protephemerida (*Protephemeroidea*) | PEN |
| | | Ephemerida [106] (*Ephemeroptera, Ephemeroidea, Plectoptera*) | PER-REC |
| | | Protodonata (*Meganisoptera*) | PEN-PER |
| | | Odonata [107] | PER-REC |
| | | Protohemiptera (*Pseudohemiptera*) | PEN-PER |
| | | Protoperlaria [108] | PER |
| | | Plecoptera (*Perlarides, Perloidea, Perlaria, Nemuraedes*) | PER-REC |
| | | Protorthoptera | PEN-PER |
| | | Caloneurodea | PEN-PER |
| | | Diploglossata (*Hemimeroidea, Dermodermaptera*) | PAL |
| | | Grylloblattoidea (*Notoptera*) | REC |
| | | Orthoptera (*Saltatoria, Aeroplanoptera*) | PEN-REC |
| | | Phasmidia (*Phasmoidea, Ambulatoria, Gressoria, Cheleutoptera*) | TRI-REC |
| | | Blattaria (*Blattaeformia, Oothecaria, Cursoria, Dictyoptera, Neoblattariae*) | PEN-REC |
| | | Mantodea (*Deratoptera, Dacnostomata, Phylloptera, Exopterygoptera, Pandictyoptera*) | PAL-REC |
| | | Glosselytrodea | PER-JUR |
| | | Protelytroptera (*Protocoleoptera*) | PER |
| | | Dermaptera (*Labidura, Euplexoptera*) | JUR-REC |
| | | Embioptera (*Embiidina, Embioidea, Adenopoda, Oligoneura, Aetioptera*) | OLI-REC |
| | | Isoptera | EOC-REC |

[103] Coleopteroidea = PROTOCOLEOPTERA + COLEOPTERA + STREPSIPTERA. Phthiraptera (Ellipoptera) = MALLOPHAGA + ANOPLURA. Hemiptera (Rhynchota) = HETEROPTERA + HOMOPTERA + PROTOHEMIPTERA + PALAEOHEMIPTERA. Blattoidea = PROTOBLATTOIDEA + BLATTARIA + MANTODEA + ISOPTERA + ZORAPTERA + PSOCOPTERA + MALLOPHAGA + ANOPLURA.

[104] *Includes:* Hemiodonata, Anisaxia, Permodictyoptera, Breyeridea, Archaehymenoptera.

[105] *Includes:* Protohymenoptera, Diaphanopteroidea, Palaeohymenoptera.

[106] *Includes:* Aphelophlebia, Agnatha, Odontota, Anisoptera, Archipterygota.

[107] *Includes:* Paraneuroptera, Permodonata, Cryptodonata, Cryptodontia, Libellulides, Libelluloidea.

[108] *Includes:* Protoblattoidea, Pruvostitoptera, Mixotermitoidea, Synarmogoi-

| Class | Subcl | Order | |
|-------|-------|-------|---|
| | | Psocoptera (*Corrodentia, Copeognatha*) | PER-REC |
| | | Zoraptera (*Panisoptera*) | REC |
| | | Mallophaga (*Lipoptera*) | REC |
| | | Thysanoptera (*Physopoda, Physapida, Thripoides, Thripsites*) | PER-REC |
| | | Homoptera | PAL-REC |
| | | Heteroptera [109] | MES-REC |
| | | Anoplura [110] (*Siphunculata, Parasita, Pseudorhynchota*) | PLE-REC |
| | Endopterygota [111] (*Holometabola*) | | PER-REC |
| | | Neuroptera [112] | PER-REC |
| | | Mecoptera (*Panorpatae, Panorpina, Mecaptera, Petanoptera, Paramecoptera, Protomecoptera, Protodiptera*) | PER-REC |
| | | Trichoptera (*Phryganoidea, Placipennes, Paratrichoptera, Agnathes*) | JUR-REC |
| | | Lepidoptera (*Glossata*) | EOC-REC |
| | | Diptera (*Antliata, Halterata, Halteriptera, Haustellata*) | JUR-REC |
| | | Siphonaptera (*Suctoria, Aphaniptera, Rophoteira, Medamoptera, Pulicina*) | OLI-REC |
| | | Coleoptera [113] (*Eleutherata, Elytroptera*) | PER-REC |
| | | Strepsiptera [114] (*Rhipiptera, Rhipidoptera, Strepsata, Stylopida*) | OLI-REC |
| | | Hymenoptera | JUR-REC |

## CHAETOGNATHA [115]

| | | | |
|---|---|---|---|
| CHAETOGNATHA | | | CAM-REC |
| | Sagittoidea | | CAM-REC |

dea, Hapalopteroidea, Hadentomoidea, Reculoidea, Cnemidolestoidea, Paraplecoptera, Miomoptera, Protocicadida, Protofulgorida.

[109] *Includes:* Palaeohemiptera, Hemipsocoptera.

[110] *Includes:* Pediculidea, Polyptera.

[111] Hymenopteroidea = ARCHAEOHYMENOPTERA + PALAEOHYMENOPTERA + PROTOHYMENOPTERA + HYMENOPTERA. Panorpoidea = TRICHOPTERA + LEPIDOPTERA + DIPTERA + SIPHONAPTERA + MEGASECOPTERA + PANORPATAE.

[112] *Includes:* Megaloptera, Raphidioidea, Emmenognatha, Leptophya. (Planipennia sometimes used for all these.)

[113] *Includes:* Paracoleoptera.

[114] Sometimes placed in Coleoptera as family Stylopidae.

[115] *Synonyms:* Homalopterygia, Oesthelminthes.

[116] *Synonyms:* Brachiata, Pogonofora.

# POGONOPHORA [116]

| | | |
|---|---|---|
| POGONOPHORA | | REC |
| Thecanephria | | REC |
| Athecanephria | | REC |

# ECHINODERMATA [117]

| | | |
|---|---|---|
| CYSTOIDEA | | ORD-PER |
| Hydrophoridea [118] (*Cystidea*) | | ORD-DEV |
| Rhombifera | | ORD-DEV |
| Diploporita | | ORD-DEV |
| Blastoidea [119] | | ORD-PER |
| Eublastoidea | | SIL-PER |
| Coronata | | ORD-SIL |
| Parablastoidea | | ORD |
| CRINOIDEA [120] (*Brachiata, Actinoidea, Eucrinoidea*) | | ORD-REC |
| Inadunata [121] | | ORD-TRI |
| Disparida (*Disparata*) | | ORD-PER |
| Hybocrinida | | ORD-SIL |
| Cladida (*Cladoidea*) | | ORD-TRI |
| Flexibilia (*Ichthyocrinacea*) | | ORD-PER |
| Taxocrinida (*Taxocrinoidea*) | | ORD-PER |
| Sagenocrinida (*Sagenocrinoidea*) | | SIL-PER |
| Camerata (*Sphaeroidocrinacea, Adunata*) | | ORD-PER |
| Diplobathrida (*Diplobathra*) | | ORD-MIS |
| Monobathrida (*Monobathra*) | | ORD-PER |
| Articulata [122] | | TRI-REC |
| Isocrinida | | TRI-REC |
| Millericrinida | | TRI-EOC |
| Cyrtocrinida | | JUR-REC |
| Uintacrinida | | CRE |
| Roveacrinida | | TRI-CRE |

[117] *Subphyla:* Pelmatozoa = CYSTOIDEA + BLASTOIDEA + CRINOIDEA + EOCRI-
NOIDEA + PARACRINOIDEA + EDRIOASTEROIDEA. Homalozoa = CARPOIDEA + MA-
CHAERIDIA. Haplozoa = single class HAPLOZOA. Eleutherozoa = SOMASTEROIDEA +
ASTEROIDEA + OPHIUROIDEA + ECHINOIDEA + BOTHROCIDAROIDEA + OPHIOCYSTO-
IDEA + HOLOTHURIOIDEA. *Includes:* Heterostelea (CARPOIDEA + Amphoridea), As-
terozoa, Stelleroidea, Stelliformia, Hypostoma, Echinozoa, Cystocidaroidea, Apo-
rita.

[118] *Includes:* Eucystoidea, Cystechinoidea, Dichoporita, Cystocrinoidea.

[119] Sometimes separated into orders Regulares and Irregulares, or orders Eublastoidea and Protoblastoidea. Sometimes as a separate class.

[120] *Includes:* Palaeocrinoidea, Inarticulata, Coadunata, Costata, Testacea, Mo-

| Class | Subcl | Order | |
|---|---|---|---|
| | | Comatulida | JUR-REC |
| EOCRINOIDEA [123] | | | CAM-ORD |
| | | Eocrinoidea | CAM-ORD |
| PARACRINOIDEA | | | ORD |
| | | Paracrinoidea | ORD |
| EDRIOASTEROIDEA (*Thecoidea, Cystasteroidea, Thyroidea,* | | | CAM-PEN |
| *Agelacrinoidea*) | | | |
| | | Edrioasteroidea | CAM-PEN |
| CARPOIDEA | | | CAM-DEV |
| | | Carpoidea | CAM-DEV |
| MACHAERIDIA [124] | | | ORD-DEV |
| | | Machaeridia | ORD-DEV |
| HAPLOZOA [124] | | | CAM |
| | | Cyamoidea | CAM |
| | | Cycloidea | CAM |
| SOMASTEROIDEA | | | ORD |
| | | Goniactinida | ORD |
| ASTEROIDEA [125] (*Cirrigrada*) | | | ORD-REC |
| | | Hemizonida | ORD-CAR |
| | | Platyasterida | ORD-DEV |
| | | Phanerozonea | ORD-REC |
| | | Spinulosa [126] | REC |
| | | Forcipulata [126] | REC |
| AULUROIDEA | | | ORD-MIS |
| | | Lysophiuroida (*Lysophiurae, Aegophiurida*) | ORD-MIS |
| | | Streptophiuroida (*Streptophiurae*) | ORD-MIS |
| OPHIUROIDEA [127] (*Spinigrada*) | | | ORD-REC |
| | Myophiurida | | ORD-DEV |
| | | Ophiocystiida | ORD-DEV |
| | | Aganasterida | ?-REC |
| | | Phrynophiurida | ?-REC |
| | | Laemophiurida | ?-REC |
| | | Gnathophiurida | ?-REC |

nocyclica, Dicyclica, Irregularia, Regularia, Larvata, Tesselata, Canaliculata, Semi-articulata.

[121] Sometimes divided into Larviformia (Haplocrinacea) and Fistulata (Cyatho-crinacea).

[122] *Includes:* Pentacrinoidea, Pentacrinacea, Stomatocrinoidea, Neocrinoidea.

[123] Perhaps not a natural group.

[124] Groups of doubtful relationships,—possibly not even Echinodermata.

[125] *Includes:* Encrinasteriae, Euasteriae, Cryptozonia.

[126] Sometimes united as Cryptozonia.

[127] *Includes:* Ophiureae, Ophiurida, Euryalae, Euryalida, Cladophiurae, Zyg-ophiurae. Also sometimes divided into orders Stenurida and Ophiurida.

| Class | Subcl | Order | |
|---|---|---|---|

| | Chilophiurida | ?-REC |
|---|---|---|

ECHINOIDEA [128] — ORD-REC

| | | |
|---|---|---|
| Regularia [129] (*Endocyclica*) | | ORD-REC |
| Lepidocentroida | | ORD-PER |
| Cidaroida | | MIS-REC |
| Centrechinoida (*Diadematoida, Diademoida*) | | CRE-REC |
| Exocycloida (*Exocyclica*) | | JUR-REC |
| Plesiocidaroida | | TRI |
| Echinocystoida | | SIL |
| Perischoechinoida | | SIL-PER |
| Irregularia [130] | | JUR-REC |
| Holectypoida | | JUR-REC |
| Cassiduloida | | JUR-REC |
| Conoclypina | | CEN |
| Clypeastroida | | CRE-REC |
| Spatangoida | | CRE-REC |

BOTHRIOCIDAROIDEA (*Pseudechinoidea*) — ORD

| Bothriocidaroida | ORD |
|---|---|

OPHIOCYSTIOIDEA (*Ophiocistioidea*) — ORD-DEV

| Ophiocystia | ORD-DEV |
|---|---|

HOLOTHURIOIDEA [131] (*Holothuroidea, Fistulides, Scytodermata, Ascidiastella, Scytactinata*) — ORD-REC

| | |
|---|---|
| Aspidochirota [132] (*Aspidochirotida*) | JUR-REC |
| Elasipoda (*Elasipodida*) | REC |
| Dendrochirota (*Cucumariida, Dendrochirotida*) | REC |
| Molpadonia (*Molpadida*) | REC |
| Apoda (*Synaptida, Paractinopoda*) | PER-REC |
| Megalopoda | ORD |

## PTEROBRANCHIA

| PTEROBRANCHIA | ORD-REC |
|---|---|
| Rhabdopleurida | CRE-REC |
| Cephalodiscidea | ORD-REC |

[128] *Includes:* Palaeo-echinoidea, Paleo-echinoidea, Palechinoidea, Euechinoidea.

[129] *Includes:* Melonechinoida, Melonitoida, Stirodonta, Aulodonta, Camarodonta, Endobranchiata, Ectobranchiata.

[130] *Includes:* Gnathostomata, Atelostomata.

[131] *Includes:* Pedata. Subclasses sometimes accepted: Actinopoda, Apoda, Megalopoda.

## ENTEROPNEUSTA[133]

| | |
|---|---|
| ENTEROPNEUSTA | REC |
| Balanoglossida | REC |

## PLANCTOSPHAEROIDEA

| | |
|---|---|
| PLANCTOSPHAEROIDEA | REC |
| Planctosphaeroidea | REC |

## TUNICATA[134]

| | |
|---|---|
| LARVACEA (*Copelata, Appendicularia, Atremata, Perennichordata*) | REC |
| Larvacea | REC |
| ASCIDIACEA [135] (*Tethyodeae*) | REC |
| Stolidobranchiata (*Ptychobranchia*) | REC |
| Aspiraculata | REC |
| Phlebobranchiata (*Diktyobranchia, Dictyobranchia*) | REC |
| Aplousobranchiata (*Krikobranchia*) | REC |
| Octacnemida | REC |
| THALIACEA | REC |
| Pyrosomata | REC |
| Pyrosomatida (*Luciae, Lucida*) | REC |
| Myosomata | REC |
| Cyclomyaria (*Doliolida*) | REC |
| Hemimyaria (*Salpida*) | REC |
| Desmomyaria | REC |

## CEPHALOCHORDATA[136]

| | |
|---|---|
| LEPTOCARDIA | REC |
| Amphioxi (*Branchiostomoidea*) | REC |

[132] *Includes:* Pelagothurida.      [133] *Synonyms:* Helminthomorpha.

[134] *Synonyms:* Urochordata. *Subphyla:* Copelata = LARVACEA; Acopa (Caducichordata) = ASCIDIACEA + THALIACEA.

[135] *Includes:* Enterogona, Pleurogona.

[136] *Synonyms:* Cirrhostomi, Entomocrania, Haplocyemata, Homomeria, Myelozoa, Pharyngobranchii, Acrania.

## VERTEBRATA[137]

AGNATHA [138] (*Monorhyncha, Monorhina*)                                                      ORD-REC

   Cephalaspidomorpha                                                          SIL-REC

      Cyclostomata [139] (*Marsipobranchii, Petromyzonoidea*)      REC

      Cephalaspida [140] (*Osteostraci, Aspidocephali, Osteo-*   SIL-DEV
      *stracoidea, Cephalaspidiformes*)

      Anaspida [141] (*Anaspidoidea*)                              SIL-DEV

   Pteraspidomorpha [142] (*Pteraspides*)                                       ORD-DEV

      Pteraspida (*Heterostraci, Pteraspidiformes*)                ORD-DEV

      Coelolepida (*Coelolepidoidea, Coelolepiformes*)             SIL-DEV

PLACODERMI [143] (*Aphetohyoidea*)                                                            SIL-PER

      Acanthodii [144] (*Acanthoglossa, Acanthodioidea*)           SIL-PER

      Arthrodira [145] (*Euarthrodira, Arthrodiroidea, Phyllo-*   SIL-DEV
      *lepida, Ptyctodontida*)

      Macropetalichthyida [146] (*Anarthrodira*)                   DEV

      Antiarchi [147] (*Antiarchoidea, Pterichthyes, Pterichthy-*   DEV
      *omorpha*)

[137] *Synonyms:* Euchorda, Craniata. Superclass Gnathostomata (Amphirhyncha, Amphirhina) = PLACODERMI + all "higher" vertebrates. Ichthyopterygii = PLACODERMI + ELASMOBRANCHII + HOLOCEPHALI + OSTEICHTHYES. Pisces (Ichthya, Eotetrapoda) = AGNATHA + PLACODERMI + CHONDRICHTHYES + OSTEICHTHYES. Haemacryma = PISCES + AMPHIBIA + REPTILIA. Haematherma = AVES + MAMMALIA. Anamnia (Ichthyopsida) = PISCES + AMPHIBIA. Amniota = REPTILIA + AVES + MAMMALIA. Tetrapoda (Cheiropterygia) = AMPHIBIA + REPTILIA + AVES + MAMMALIA. Sauropsida = REPTILIA + AVES. *Includes:* Protichthyes, Ichthyodorulites.

[138] Ostracodermi (Ostracophori) = CEPHALASPIDA + ANASPIDA + PTERASPIDA + COELOLEPIDA. *Includes:* Euphaneroidea.

[139] *Includes:* Myxinoidea, Hyperotreti, Myxini, Myxiniformes, Petromyzontia, Petromyzontiformes, Hyperoarti.

[140] *Includes:* Tremataspidiformes, Lasaniiformes, Oligocnemata, Endeiolepiformes.

[141] *Includes:* Birkeniiformes, Phlebolepiformes.

[142] *Includes:* Astraspiformes, Psammosteiformes, Cyathaspiformes, Amphiaspiformes, Thelodonti.

[143] Coccostei (Coccosteomorphi) = EUARTHRODIRA + PHYLLOLEPIDA + MACROPETALICHTHYES.

[144] *Includes:* Climatiiformes, Mesacanthiformes, Ischnacanthiformes, Gyracanthiformes, Cheiracanthiformes, Acanthodiformes, Acanthoessi, Acanthoessiformes. Conodontophorida (Conodonta) may belong here (Ord-Tri).

[145] *Includes:* Acanthothoraci, Arctolepiformes, Acanthaspidomorphi, Acanthaspida, Coccosteiformes, Brachythoraci, Mylostomatiformes, Ptyctodontiformes, Phyllolepiformes.

[146] *Includes:* Gemuendiniformes, Rhenanida, Petalichthyida.

[147] *Includes:* Remigolepiformes, Asterolepiformes.

|  |  |
|---|---|
| Stegoselachii (*Stensiöelliformes, Jagoriniformes, Stensiöellida*) | SIL-MIS |
| Palaeospondyloidea (*Palaeospondyliformes*) | DEV |
| CHONDRICHTHYES | DEV-REC |
| Elasmobranchii [148] | DEV-REC |
| Cladoselachii [149] (*Pleuropterygii*) | DEV-PER |
| Pleuracanthodii (*Ichthyotomi, Proselachii*) | DEV-TRI |
| Selachii [150] (*Euselachii, Plagiostomi, Chondropterygii, Placoidei*) | DEV-REC |
| Batoidea [151] (*Hypotremata, Platosomia*) | JUR-REC |
| Holocephali [152] | DEV-REC |
| Bradyodonti [153] (*Bradyodontoidea*) | DEV-PER |
| Chimaerae [154] (*Chimaeroidea*) | JUR-REC |
| OSTEICHTHYES (*Teleostomi*) | DEV-REC |
| Actinopterygii [155] | DEV-REC |
| Chondrostei [156] (*Chondrosteoidea, Palaeopterygii*) | DEV-REC |
| Holostei [157] | PER-REC |
| Teleostei [158] | JUR-REC |

[148] *Includes:* Diplodonti, Diplodontiformes, Xenanthi, Xenacanthi, Xenacanthoidea.

[149] *Includes:* Cladodontiformes, Cladoselachoidea, Cladoselachiformes.

[150] Includes: Pleurostomata, Pleurotremata, Selachoidea, Heterodontiformes, Heterodontoidea, Hexanchoidea, Hexanchiformes, Notidanoidea, Lamnoidea, Lamniformes, Isuriformes, Galeoidei, Squaloidea, Squaliformes, Tectospondyli, Edestidi.

[151] *Includes:* Narcaciontiformes, Torpediniformes, Rajiformes.

[152] *Includes:* Petalodontes, Petalodontiformes.

[153] *Includes:* Eubradyodonti, Chondrenchelyes, Chondrenchelyiformes.

[154] *Includes:* Chimaeriformes.

[155] Sometimes divided into superorders: CHONDROSTEI, HOLOSTEI, TELEOSTEI. Sometimes divided into infraclasses: Polypterei, CHONDROSTEI, HOLOSTEI, TELEOSTEI. Ganoidi = CHONDROSTEI + HOLOSTEI. Neopterygii = HOLOSTEI + TELEOSTEI.

[156] *Includes:* Tarrasiiformes, Gymnonisciformes, Luganoidiiformes, Phanerorhynchiformes, Dorypteriformes, Cephaloxeniformes, Bobasatraniiformes, Redfieldiiformes, Calopteriformes, Perleidiformes, Platysiagiformes, Ospiiformes, Aetheodontiformes, Pholidopleuriformes, Saurichthyiformes, Palaeoniscoidea, Heterocerci, Palaeonisciformes, Polypterini, Brachypterygii, Polypteriformes, Cladistia, Cladistioidea, Acipenseroidea, Acipenseriformes, Subholostei, Subholosteoidea.

[157] *Includes:* Semionotoidea, Lepidostei, Lepisostei, Lepidosteoidea, Lepisosteiformes, Ginglymodi, Rhomboganoidei, Pycnodontoidea, Pycnodontiformes, Aspidorhynchoidea, Aspidorhynchiformes, Amioidea, Amiiformes, Pholidophoroidea, Pholidophoriformes, Pachycormoidea, Pachycormiformes, Protospondyli.

[158] *See* p. 66 for footnote 158.

| Class | Subcl | Order | |
|-------|-------|-------|--|
| | | Choanichthyes (*Amphibioidea*) | DEV-REC |
| | | Crossopterygii [159] (*Crossopterygioidea*) | DEV-REC |
| | | Dipnoi [160] | DEV-REC |
| AMPHIBIA [161] (*Batrachia*) | | | DEV-REC |
| | Labyrinthodontia [162] (*Stegocephalia*) | | DEV-TRI |
| | | Ichthyostegalia | DEV-PEN |
| | | Rhachitomi | MIS-TRI |
| | | Embolomeri | MIS-PER |
| | | Trematosauria | MES |
| | | Stereospondyli | TRI |
| | Salientia [163] | | PEN-REC |
| | | Eoanura | PEN |
| | | Proanura | TRI |
| | | Anura [164] (*Euanura, Ecaudata*) | JUR-REC |
| | Lepospondyli (*Urodeloidei, Pseudocentrophori*) | | MIS-REC |
| | | Aistopoda | PEN |
| | | Nectridia | PEN-PER |
| | | Microsauria (*Adelospondyli, Micramphibia*) | MIS-PER |
| | | Urodela (*Caudata, Gradientia, Saurabatrachia*) | CRE-REC |
| | | Apoda (*Gymnophiona, Peromela, Caecilia*) | REC |

[158] *Includes:* Isospondyli, Isospondyloidea, Malacopterygii, Thrissomorphi, Ostariophysi, Ostariophysoidea, Apodes, Heteromi, Heteromoidea, Mesichthyes, Cyprinodontiformes, Acanthopterygii, Symbranchiformes, Physostomi, Physoclysti, Discocephalioidea, Echiniiformes, Echeniiformes, Plectognathoidea, Hypostomosoidea, Cephalacanthoidea, Scleropareioidea, Percomorphoidea, Allotriognathoidea, Anacanthoidea, Apodoidea, Batrachoidea, Batrachoidiformes, Haplodoci, Gobiesociformes, Xenopterygii, Lampridiformes, Lophiiformes, Lyomeroidea, Pediculati, Pediculatiformes, Pegasiformes, Salmopercoidea, Solenichthyoidea, Synentognathoidea, Tetradontiformes, Tetrodontiformes, Thoracostoidea, Thunniformes, Icosteioidea, Icosteiformes, Malacichthyes, Chaudhurioidea, Chaudhuriiformes, Mastacembelioidea, Mastacembeliformes, Opisthomi, Synbranchioidea, Perciformes, Dactylopteriformes, Pleuronectoidea, Pleuronectiformes, Heterosomata, Beryciformes, Berycomorphoidea, Zeiformes, Zeomorphoidea, Mugiliformes, Polynemiformes, Ophiocephaliformes, Clupeiformes, Bathyclupeoidea, Bathyclupeiformes, Galaxiiformes, Cypriniformes, Anguilliformes, Halosauriformes, Notacanthiformes, Beloniformes, Myctophiformes, Iniomi, Scopeliformes, Ateleopiformes, Ateleopoidea, Giganturoidea, Giganturiformes, Saccopharyngiformes, Mormyroidea, Mormyriformes, Gadiformes, Macruriformes, Gasterosteiformes, Syngnathiformes, Cyprinodontoidea, Microcyprini, Phallostethiformes, Percopseiformes, Stephanoberyciformes.

[159] *Includes:* Porolepiformes, Osteolepiformes, Osteolepides, Osteolepidoti, Holoptychiformes, Megalichthyiformes, Rhipidistia, Actinistia, Coelacanthini, Coelacanthiformes.

[160] *Includes:* Dipteri, Dipteriformes, Dipneumona, Dipneusti, Phaneropleuri-

| Class | Subcl | Order | |
|---|---|---|---|
| REPTILIA | | | PEN-REC |
| | Anapsida [165] (*Parareptilia, Reptiliomorphoidea*) | | PEN-REC |
| | | Seymouriamorpha | PEN-PER |
| | | Cotylosauria | PEN-TRI |
| | | Chelonia (*Testudinata, Testudines*) | PER-REC |
| | Parapsida (*Ichthyopterygia, Metapsida*) | | TRI-CRE |
| | | Ichthyosauria | TRI-CRE |
| | Euryapsida (*Synaptosauria*) | | PER-CRE |
| | | Protorosauria [166] (*Araeoscelida*) | PER-TRI |
| | | Sauropterygia [167] | TRI-CRE |
| | Diapsida [168] | | PER-REC |
| | | Eosuchia [169] (*Prolacertiformes*) | PER-EOC |
| | | Rhynchocephalia [170] | TRI-REC |
| | | Squamata [171] (*Plagiotremata*) | JUR-REC |
| | | Thecodontia [172] | TRI |
| | | Crocodilia [173] (*Loricata, Emydosauria, Hydrosauria*) | TRI-REC |
| | | Pterosauria (*Pterodactyli, Ornithosauria*) | JUR-CRE |

formes, Uronemiformes, Ctenodontiformes, Ceratodontiformes, Lepidosireniformes, Rhynchodipteriformes, Monopneumona, Ctenodipterini, Ceratodonti, Sirenoidei.

[161] *Includes:* Pholidota, Monopnoa, Dipnoa, Nuda. Aspidospondyli (Apsidospondyli, Batrachosauria) = LABYRINTHODONTIA + SALIENTIA. Euamphibia = SALIENTIA + LEPOSPONDYLI.

[162] Sometimes treated as the only superorder in subclass Aspidospondyli. *Includes:* Temnospondyli, Anthracomorphoidea, Anthracosauroidea, Anthracosauria, Phyllospondyli. Seymouriamorpha removed to Reptilia.

[163] Sometimes listed as a superorder of Aspidospondyli.

[164] *Includes:* Amphicoela, Angusticoela, Opisthocoela, Anomocoela, Procoela, Diplasiocoela.

[165] *Includes:* Eunotosauria, Diadecta, Diadectomorpha, Procolophonia, Pareiasauria.

[166] *Includes:* Weigeltisauria, Trachelosauria, Tanysitrachelia.

[167] *Includes:* Nothosauria, Placodontia, Plesiosauria.

[168] Lepidosauria (Archosauromorpha) = EOSUCHIA + SQUAMATA + RHYNCHOCEPHALIA. Archosauria = THECODONTIA + CROCODILIA + PTEROSAURIA + SAURISCHIA + ORNITHISCHIA. *Includes*: Katapsida, Kathapsida, Neosauromorpha. Dinosauria (Ornithoscelida, Pachypodes) = SAURISCHIA + ORNITHISCHIA.

[169] *Includes:* Thalattosauria, Pleurosauria, Acrosauria.

[170] Sometimes placed in Archosauria.

[171] *Includes:* Sauria, Lacertilia, Serpentes, Ophidia, Pythonomorpha, Mosasauria, Rhiptoglossa, Streptostylica.

[172] *Includes:* Pseudosuchia, Phytosauria, Parasuchia.

[173] *Includes:* Protosuchia, Sebecosuchia, Mesosuchia, Thalattosuchia, Eusuchia.

| Class | Subcl | Order | |
|---|---|---|---|

          Saurischia [174] (*Theropoda, Sauropoda, Compsognatha*)  TRI-CRE

          Ornithischia (*Orthopoda, Ornithopoda, Predentata* TRI-CRE
            *Stegosauria*)

    Synapsida [175]                     PEN-JUR

          Pelycosauria            PEN-TRI

          Therapsida [176]         PER-TRI

          Ictidosauria            TRI-JUR

          Mesosauria (*Proganosauria*)    PER

AVES                             JUR-REC

    Archaeornithes (*Saururae*)         JUR

          Archaeopteryges (*Archaeopterygiformes*)   JUR

    Neornithes [177] (*Ornithae, Ornithurae*)  CRE-REC

          Hesperornithes (*Odontolcae, Hesperornithiformes*)  CRE-EOC

          Ichthyornithes (*Odontormae, Ichthyornes, Ichthyor-*  CRE
            *nithiformes, Ichthyorniformes*)

          Sphenisci (*Sphenisciformes, Impennes*)  OLI-REC

          Caenagnathae (*Caenagnathiformes*)   CRE

          Struthiones (*Struthioniformes*)   PLI-REC

          Rheae (*Rheiformes*)   PLI-REC

          Casuarii (*Casuariiformes*)   PLE-REC

          Dinornithes (*Dinornithiformes*)   PLE

          Aepyornithes (*Aepyornithiformes*)   EOC-PLE

          Apteryges (*Apterygiformes*)   PLE-REC

          Crypturi (*Tinami, Tinamiformes, Crypturiformes*)  PLI-REC

          Gaviae (*Gaviiformes*)   EOC-REC

          Podicipedes (*Podicipediformes, Podicipiformes, Colym-* OLI-REC
            *bae, Colymbiformes, Pygopodes*)

          Procellariae (*Procellariiformes, Cecomorphae, Turbi-* EOC-REC
            *nares, Tubinares*)

---

[174] *Includes:* Hallopoda.

[175] *Includes:* Promammalia (Protodonta), at one time placed in subclass Prototheria, of Mammalia.

[176] *Includes:* Dromosauria, Deinocephalia, Dicynodontia, Theriodontia, Anomodontia, Theromorpha.

[177] *Includes:* Dromeognathae, Megistanes, Gastornithes, Stereornithes, Carinatae, Colymbomorphae, Pelargomorphae, Alectoromorphae, Coraciomorphae, Limicolae, Pterocletes, Picariae, Musophagi. Neognathae (Euornithes) = all except HESPERORNITHES + ICHTHYORNITHES + IMPENNES. Superorder Odontognathae = HESPERORNITHES (+ ICHTHYORNITHES). Superorder Palaeognathae = CAENAGNATHAE + STRUTHIONES + RHEAE + CASUARII + DINORNITHES + AEPYORNITHES + APTERYGES. Ratitae included STRUTHIONES, RHEAE, CASUARII, DINOR-

| Class | Subcl | Order | |
|---|---|---|---|

Steganopodes (*Pelecani, Pelecaniformes, Pelicaniformes*) — CRE-REC

Ciconiae [178] (*Ciconiiformes, Gressores, Herodiones Herodii*) — CRE-REC

Anseres (*Anseriformes, Chenomorphae*) — CRE-REC

Falcones [179] (*Falconiformes, Accipitres, Accipitriformes*) — EOC-REC

Galli [180] (*Galliformes, Gallinae*) — EOC-REC

Grues [181] (*Gruiformes*) — EOC-REC

Diatrymae (*Diatrymiformes*) — EOC

Charadriae [182] (*Charadriiformes, Laro-limicolae*) — EOC-REC

Columbae (*Columbiformes*) — MIO-REC

Psittaci (*Psittaciformes*) — MIO-REC

Cuculi (*Coccyges, Cuculiformes*) — OLI-REC

Striges (*Strigiformes*) — EOC-REC

Caprimulgi (*Caprimulgiformes*) — PLI-REC

Macrochires (*Macrochiriformes, Apoda, Apodiformes, Micropodi, Micropodiformes*) — OLI-REC

Colii (*Colliformes*) — REC

Trogones (*Trogoniformes*) — OLI-REC

Coraciae [183] (*Coraciiformes*) — EOC-REC

Pici (*Piciformes*) — EOC-REC

Passeres [184] (*Passeriformes*) — EOC-REC

MAMMALIA [185] (*Mammifera*) — JUR-REC

Prototheria — PLE-REC

Monotremata (*Ornithodelphia*) — PLE-REC

Allotheria [186] — JUR-EOC

Multituberculata — JUR-EOC

Triconodonta — JUR

---

NITHES, AEPYORNITHES, APTERYGES, CURSORES, PROCERES, BREVIPENNES, CRYPTURI.

[178] *Includes:* Phoenicopteri, Phoenicopteriformes, Amphimorphae, Pelargiformes.

[179] *Includes:* Cathartidiformes.

[180] *Includes:* Opisthocomi, Opisthocomiformes, Heteromorphae, Grallae.

[181] *Includes:* Ralliformes, Heliornithiformes, Hemipodii, Telmatomorphormes.

[182] *Includes:* Alciformes, Lariformes.

[183] *Includes:* Alcedines, Bucerotes.

[184] *Includes:* Eurylaemi, Menurae. Scansores = PICI + PSITTACI in part.

[185] Eplacentalia = PROTOTHERIA + ALLOTHERIA + PANTOTHERIA. Theria = PANTOTHERIA + METATHERIA + EUTHERIA. Promammalia transferred to Reptilia (Synaptida).

[186] *Includes:* Plagiaulacoidea, Tritylodontoidea.

| Class | Subcl | Order | |
|-------|-------|-------|---|
| | | Pantotheria | JUR |
| | | Trituberculata | JUR |
| | | Symmetrodonta | JUR |
| | Metatheria [187] | | CRE-REC |
| | | Marsupialia (*Didelphia*) | CRE-REC |
| | Eutheria [188] (*Monodelphia, Placentalia, Placentaria*) | | CRE-REC |
| | | Insectivora | CRE-REC |
| | | Dermoptera | EOC-REC |
| | | Chiroptera | EOC-REC |
| | | Primates [189] | EOC-REC |
| | | Tillodontia | EOC |
| | | Taeniodonta (*Ganodonta, Stylinodontia*) | EOC |
| | | Edentata (*Xenarthra, Paratheria, Bruta*) | EOC-REC |
| | | Pholidota (*Squamata, Nomarthra*) | OLI-REC |
| | | Lagomorpha (*Duplicidentata*) | EOC-REC |
| | | Rodentia[190] | EOC-REC |
| | | Cetacea [191] (*Mutica, Cete*) | EOC-REC |
| | | Carnivora [192] | EOC-REC |
| | | Condylarthra | EOC |
| | | Litopterna | EOC-PLE |

[187] *Includes:* Polyprotodontia, Caenolestoidea, Diprotodontia, Paucituberculata.

[188] *Includes:* Ancylopoda, Chalicotheria, Taxeopoda, Quadrumana, Daubentomioidea, Subungulata, Pithecoidea, Platyrhina, Simiae, Toxodontia, Barytheria, Carnivores, Edentates, Ungulates, Bunotheria. Unguiculata = INSECTIVORA + DERMOPTERA + CHIROPTERA + PRIMATES + TILLODONTIA + TAENIODONTA + EDENTATA + PHOLIDOTA. Ungulata = Protungulata (CONDYLARTHRA + LITOPTERNA + NOTOUNGULATA + ASTRAPOTHERIA + TUBULIDENTATA) + Paenungulata (PANTODONTA + DINOCERATA + XENUNGULATA + PYROTHERIA + PROBOSCIDEA + EMBRITHOPODA + HYRACOIDEA + DESMOSTYLIFORMES + SIRENIA + PERISSODACTYLA + ARTIODACTYLA). Glires = LAGOMORPHA + RODENTIA. Mutilata = CETACEA + SIRENIA. Protungulata = CONDYLARTHRA + LITOPTERA + NOTOUNGULATA + ASTRAPOTHERIA + TUBULIDENTATA. Therictoidea = INSECTIVORA + Ferae. Archonta = Menotyphla + DERMOPTERA + CHIROPTERA + PRIMATES. Paenungulata = PANTODONTA + DINOCERATA + PYROTHERIA + PROBOSCIDEA + EMBRITHOPODA + HYRACOIDEA + SIRENIA. Diplarthra = PERISSODACTYLA + ARTIODACTYLA.

[189] *Includes:* Anthropoidea, Lemuroidea, Prosimii.
[190] *Includes:* Simplicidentata.
[191] *Includes:* Zeuglodontia, Archaeoceti, Odontoceti, Mystacoceti.
[192] *Includes:* Fissipedia, Creodonta, Pinnipedia, Ferungulata, Ferae.
[193] *Includes:* Taxodontia.
[194] *Includes:* Amblydactyla, Taligrada, Coryphodontia.
[195] *Includes:* Myohyracoidea.

| | |
|---|---|
| Notoungulata [193] | EOC-PLE |
| Astrapotheria | EOC-MIO |
| Tubulidentata | EOC-REC |
| Pantodonta [194] (*Amblypoda*) | EOC-OLI |
| Dinocerata (*Uintatheria*) | EOC |
| Pyrotheria | EOC-OLI |
| Proboscidea | EOC-REC |
| Embrithopoda (*Barypoda*) | OLI |
| Hyracoidea [195] (*Hyraces*) | OLI-REC |
| Sirenia | EOC-REC |
| Perissodactyla (*Mesaxonia*) | EOC-REC |
| Artiodactyla (*Paraxonia*) | EOC-REC |

# BIBLIOGRAPHY

MANY BOOKS, pamphlets, and articles have been consulted in the preparation of this classification. A listing of all of these appears to serve no essential purpose here. The list given below therefore contains principally recent works in which a formal classification is presented for the entire animal kingdom or a major part of it. The list is intended merely as background for the present classification. It does not contain references to all authors and works cited in the text.

Boettger, C. R.
  1952. Die Stämme des Tierreichs in ihrer systematischen Gliederung. Abhandl. Braunschweigischen Wiss. Gesell., Band IV, pp. 238–300.
Borradaile, L. A., Potts, F. A., Eastham, L. E. S., and Saunders, J. T.
  1951. The Invertebrata. A manual for the use of students, 2nd edition, 725 pp. Cambridge Univ. Press, Cambridge.
Brues, C. T., Melander, A. L., and Carpenter, F. M.
  1954. Classification of insects. Museum of Comparative Zoology, Bull. 108, pp. 1–917.
Colbert, E. H.
  1955. Evolution of the vertebrates. A history of the backboned animals through time, 479 pp. John Wiley & Sons, New York.
Dawes, B.
  1956. The Trematoda, with special reference to British and other European forms, 644 pp. Cambridge Univ. Press, Cambridge.
Forster-Cooper, C.
  1951. A text-book of zoology, by T. J. Parker and W. A. Haswell, 6th edition, vol. 2, 758 pp. Macmillan & Co., London.
Hadži, J.
  1953. An attempt to reconstruct animal classification. Systematic Zoology, vol. 2, pp. 145–154.
Hall, R. P.
  1953. Protozoology, 682 pp. Prentice-Hall, New York.
Hyman, L. H.
  1940. The invertebrates: Protozoa through Ctenophora, 726 pp. McGraw-Hill Book Co., New York.
  1951. The invertebrates: Platyhelminthes and Rhynchocoela. The acoelomate Bilateria, vol. II, 550 pp. McGraw-Hill Book Co., New York.
  1951. The invertebrates: Acanthocephala, Aschelminthes, and Entoprocta. The

pseudocoelomate Bilateria, vol. III, 572 pp. McGraw-Hill Book Co., New York.

1955. The invertebrates: Echinodermata. The Coelomate Bilateria, vol. IV, 763 pp. McGraw-Hill Book Co., New York.

1959. The invertebrates: Smaller coelomate groups. Chaetognatha, Hemichordata, Pogonophora, Phoronida, Ectoprocta, Brachiopoda, Sipunculida. The coelomate Bilateria, vol. V, 783 pp. McGraw-Hill Book Co., New York.

Kerkut, G. A.

1958. The Invertebrata, by Borradaile, Potts, et al., 3rd edition, 795 pp. Cambridge Univ. Press, Cambridge.

Kudo, R. R.

1954. Protozoology, 4th edition, 966 pp. Charles C. Thomas, Springfield, Illinois.

Lowenstein, O.

1954. A text-book of zoology, by T. J. Parker and W. A. Haswell, 6th edition, vol. 1, 770 pp. Macmillan & Co., London.

Mayr, E. and Amadon, D.

1951. A classification of recent birds. American Museum Novitates, No. 1496, pp. 1–42.

Mayr, E., Linsley, E. G., and Usinger, R. L.

1953. Methods and principles of systematic zoology, 328 pp. McGraw-Hill Book Co., New York.

Moore, R. C. (editor)

1953–1961. Treatise of invertebrate paleontology.
    (Issued in parts with numerous contributors)

D. Protista 3. Protozoa (chiefly Radiolaria and Tintinnina), 195 pp. 1954. (By A. S. Campbell and R. C. Moore)

E. Archaeocyatha and Porifera, 122 pp. 1955. (By V. J. Okulitch and M. W. de Laubenfels)

F. Coelenterata, 498 pp. 1956. (By F. M. Bayer, H. Boschma, H. J. Harrington, D. Hill, L. H. Hyman, M. Lecompte, E. Montanaro-Gallitelli, R. C. Moore, E. C. Stumm, J. W. Wells)

G. Bryozoa, 253 pp. 1953. (By R. S. Bassler)

I. Mollusca 1. Mollusca—General features. Scaphopoda. Amphineura. Monoplacophora. Gastropoda—General features. Archaeogastropoda and some (mainly Paleozoic) Caenogastropoda and Opisthobranchia, 351 pp. 1960. (By J. B. Knight, L. R. Cox, A. M. Keen, A. G. Smith, R. L. Batten, E. L. Yochelson, N. H. Ludbrook, R. Robertson, C. M. Yonge, R. C. Moore)

L. Mollusca IV. Cephalopoda, Ammonoidea, 490 pp. 1957. (By W. J. Arkell, W. M. Furnish, B. Kummel, A. K. Miller, R. C. Moore, O. H. Schindewolf, P. C. Sylvester-Bradley, C. W. Wright)

O. Arthropoda 1. Arthropoda—General features. Protarthropoda. Euarthropoda—General features. Trilobitomorpha, 560 pp. 1959. (By H. J. Harrington, G. Henningsmoen, B. F. Howell, V. Jaanusson, C. Lochman-

Balk, R. C. Moore, C. Paulsen, F. Rasetti, E. Richter, R. Richter, H. Schmidt, K. Sdzuy, W. Struve, L. Størmer, C. J. Stubblefield, R. Tripp, J. M. Weller, H. B. Whittington)

P. Arthropoda 2. Chelicerata with sections on Pycnogonida and Palaeoisopus, 181 pp. 1955. (By L. Størmer, A. Petrunkevitch, J. W. Hedgpeth)

Q. Arthropoda 3. Crustacea, Ostracoda, 442 pp. 1961. (By R. H. Benson, J. M. Berdan, W. A. van den Bold, T. Hanai, I. Hessland, H. V. Howe, R. V. Kesling, S. A. Levinson, R. A. Reyment, R. C. Moore, H. W. Scott, R. H. Shaver, I. G. Sohn, L. E. Stover, F. M. Swain, P. C. Sylvester-Bradley, J. Wainwright)

V. Graptolithina with sections on Enteropneusta and Pterobranchia, 101 pp. 1955. (By O. M. B. Bulman)

Moore, R. C., Lalicker, C. G., and Fischer, A. G.

1952. Invertebrate fossils, 766 pp. McGraw-Hill Book Co., New York.

Noble, G. K.

1931. The biology of the Amphibia, 577 pp. McGraw-Hill Book Co., New York. (Reprinted 1954, Dover Publications, New York)

Parker, T. J. and Haswell, W. A.

1897. A text-book of zoology, vol. I, 779 pp. Macmillan & Co., London.

Pearse, A. S.

1949. Zoological names. A list of phyla, classes, and orders, 24 pp. Zoology Department, Duke Univ., Durham, N. C.

Piveteau, J.

1953. Traité de Paléontologie, tome III, 1063 pp. Masson et Cie., Paris. (Onychophores, Arthropodes, Échinodermes, Stomocordés)

Romer, A. S.

1945. Vertebrate paleontology, 2nd edition, 687 pp. Univ. of Chicago Press, Chicago.

Rothschild, (Lord).

1961. A classification of living animals, 106 pp. Longmans, Green & Co., Ltd. London.

Shrock, R. R. and Twenhofel, W. H.

1953. Principles of invertebrate paleontology, 816 pp. McGraw-Hill Book Co., New York.

Simpson, G. G.

1945. The principles of classification and a classification of mammals. Bull. American Museum Natural History, vol. 85, 350 pp.

Wardle, R. A. and McLeod, J. A.

1952. The zoology of tapeworms, 780 pp. Univ. of Minnesota Press, Minneapolis.

Waterman, T. H. and Chace, F. A., Jr.

1960. General crustacean biology, pp. 1–33, in The physiology of Crustacea, edited by T. H. Waterman, vol. 1, 670 pp. Academic Press, New York.

Wetmore, A.

1960. A classification for the birds of the World. Smithsonian Miscellaneous Collections, vol. 139, No. 11, pp. 1–37.

# INDEX TO COMMON NAMES

aardvarks, 25
acorn-worms, 22
albatrosses, 24
alligators, 23
alpacas, 25
amphibians, 23
angel-fishes, 23
angle-worms, 17
animalcules
    bear-animalcules, 7, 17
    sun-animalcules, 9
    wheel-animalcules, 6, 13
animals
    one-celled animals, 6
anis, 24
annelids, 16
antbirds, 25
anteaters, 25
antelopes, 25
ant-lions, 20
ants, 21
    velvet-ants, 21
    white-ants, 20
apes, 25
aphids, 20
arachnids, 7, 18
argonauts, 16
armadillos, 25
arrow-worms, 7, 21
arthropods, 17
ascidians, 22
avocets, 24
awks, 24
aye-aye, 25

babblers, 25
baboons, 25
badgers, 25
bandicoots, 25
barbets, 24
bark-lice, 20
barnacles, 18
basket-stars, 21
batrachians, 23
bats, 25
bear-animalcules, 7, 17
beard-worms, 7, 21
bears, 25
    water-bears, 7, 17
    woolly-bears, 20

beavers, 25
bed-bugs, 20
bee-eaters, 24
bees, 21
beetles, 20
bird-lice, 20
birds, 23
    antbirds, 25
    blackbirds, 25
    bowerbirds, 25
    butcher-birds, 25
    frigate-birds, 24
    humming-birds, 24
    mockingbirds, 25
    mouse-birds, 24
    oil-birds, 24
    ovenbirds, 25
    puffbirds, 24
    secretary-birds, 24
    snakebirds, 24
    songbirds, 25
    surf-birds, 24
    tropicbirds, 24
    wattlebirds, 25
    weaverbirds, 25
birds-of-paradise, 25
biting-lice, 20
bitterns, 24
bivalves, 16
blackbirds, 25
black-corals, 12
black-widows, 18
bloodsuckers, 17
blue-corals, 11
blues, 20
boat-shells, 16
bony fishes, 23
boobies, 24
book-lice, 20
book-scorpions, 18
bots, 20
bowerbirds, 25
brachiopods, 15
brine-shrimps, 18
bristle-tails, 20
brittle-stars, 21
broadbills, 25
bryozoans, 15
bugs, 20
    bed-bugs, 20
    croton-bugs, 20
    mealy-bugs, 20
    pillbugs, 19

bugs (*Continued*)
    sowbugs, 19
    spittle-bugs, 20
bulbuls, 25
buntings, 25
bush-babies, 25
bustard-quails, 24
bustards, 24
butcher-birds, 25
butterflies, 20
butterfly-shells, 16

Caddis-flies, 20
caecilians, 23
cake-urchins, 22
calcareous sponges, 10
camels, 25
campodeids, 20
capybaras, 25
caracaras, 24
cartilaginous fishes, 23
case-flies, 20
cassowaries, 24
caterpillars, 20
cats, 25
cattle, 25
caymans, 23
centipedes, 19
cephalopods, 16
chalky sponges, 10
chiggers, 18
chigoes, 20
chimaeras, 23
chimpanzees, 25
chinchillas, 25
chipmunks, 25
chitons, 15
cicadas, 20
ciliates, 10
civets, 25
clams, 16
coatis, 25
coccolithophores, 9
coccoliths, 9
cockroaches, 20
coelacanths, 23
coelenterates, 11
colies, 24
colugos, 25
comb-jellies, 6, 12
coots, 24
corallines, 15

corals, 6, 11
  black-corals, 12
  blue-corals, 11
  hexacorals, 11
  horny-corals, 11
  soft-corals, 11
  stony-corals, 11
  thorny-corals, 12
cormorants, 24
crabs, 19
  horseshoe-crabs, 17
craniates, 35
cranes, 24
crayfish, 19
creepers, 25
crickets, 20
  mole-crickets, 20
crinoids, 21
crocodiles, 23
croton-bugs, 20
crows, 25
crustaceans, 7, 18
cuckoos, 24
cuttle-fish, 16

daddy-long-legs, 18
damselflies, 20
deer, 25
devil's-darning-needles, 20
dinoflagellates, 9
dippers, 25
divers, 24
dobson-flies, 20
dodos, 24
dogfishes, 23
dogs, 25
dolphins, 25
dormice, 25
doves, 24
dragonflies, 20
drongos, 25
ducks, 24
dust-lice, 20

eagles, 24
ear-shells, 15
earthworms, 17
earwigs, 20
echidna, 25
echinoderms, 21
eels
  slime-eels, 23
elaters, 20
elephants, 25
embiids, 20
emus, 24
endoprocts, 14

fairy-shrimps, 18
falcons, 24
false-scorpions, 18
feather-stars, 21
finches, 25
fireflies, 20
fishes
  angel-fishes, 23
  bony fishes, 23
  cartilaginous fishes, 23
  crayfish, 19
  cuttle-fish, 16
  dogfishes, 23
  hag-fishes, 23
  jawless fishes, 23
  lobe-finned fishes, 23
  lungfishes, 23
  rabbit-fishes, 23
  ratfishes, 23
  ray-finned fishes, 23
  silver-fish, 20
  starfishes, 21
fish-flies, 20
flagellates, 9
  animal-like, 9
  plant-like, 9
flamingoes, 24
flatworms, 6, 12
fleas, 20
  snow-fleas, 20
  water-fleas, 18
flies, 20
  butterflies, 20
  caddis-flies, 20
  case-flies, 20
  damselflies, 20
  dobson-flies, 20
  dragonflies, 20
  fireflies, 20
  fish-flies, 20
  ichneumon-flies, 21
  lantern-flies, 20
  mayflies, 20
  orl-flies, 20
  salmon-flies, 20
  sawflies, 20
  scorpion-flies, 20
  serpent-flies, 20
  snake-flies, 20
  stone-flies, 20
  trout-flies, 20
  white-flies, 20
flukes, 12
flycatchers, 25
flying-lemurs, 25
foraminiferans, 9
forams, 9
fowls, 24
foxes, 25
frigate-birds, 24
frogmouths, 24

frogs, 23
frog-spit, 20
fulmars, 24

gallinules, 24
gall-wasps, 21
gannets, 24
gars, 23
gastropods, 15
gastrotrichs, 13
gavials, 23
gazelles, 25
geese, 24
gibbons, 25
giraffes, 25
glass-sponges, 10
gnats, 20
glow-worms, 20
goats, 25
goatsuckers, 24
gordian-worms, 6, 14
gorgonians, 11
gorillas, 25
graptolites, 27
grasshoppers, 20
grebes, 24
grosbeaks, 25
grouse, 24
grylloblattids, 20
guanacos, 25
guenons, 25
guinea-pigs, 25
gulls, 24

hag-fishes, 23
hammerheads, 24
hares, 25
  sea-hares, 15
harriers, 24
harvest-men, 18
hawks, 24
heart-urchins, 21, 22
hedgehogs, 25
herons, 24
hexacorals, 11
hippopotamuses, 25
hoatzins, 24
honey-creepers, 25
honey-guides, 24
hoopoes, 24
hornbills, 24
hornets, 21
horntails, 21
horny-corals, 11
horny-sponges, 10
horsehair-worms, 6, 14
horses, 25
horseshoe-crabs, 17
humming-birds, 24

hydroids, 6
hydrozoans, 31
hyenas, 25
hyraxes, 25

ibises, 24
ichneumon-flies, 21
insectivores, 25
insects, 7, 20
    leaf-insects, 20
    scale-insects, 20
    stick-insects, 20

jacamars, 24
jacanas, 24
japygids, 20
jawless fishes, 23
jays, 25
jellyfishes, 6, 11

kagus, 24
kangaroo-rats, 25
kangaroos, 25
katydids, 20
kingfishers, 24
kinglets, 25
kinkajous, 25
kiwis, 24
koalas, 25
krill, 19

lace-wings, 20
lampreys, 23
lamp-shells, 7, 15
lancelets, 7, 23
land-snails, 16
langurs, 25
lantern-flies, 20
larks, 25
lars, 25
leaf-hoppers, 20
leaf-insects, 20
leeches, 17
lemmings, 25
lemurs, 25
    flying-lemurs, 25
lice, 20
    bark-lice, 20
    bird-lice, 20
    biting-lice, 20
    book-lice, 20
    dust-lice, 20
    sucking lice, 20
limpets, 15
limpkins, 24

lions
    ant-lions, 20
    sea-lions, 25
lizards, 23
llamas, 25
lobe-finned fishes, 23
lobsters, 19
locusts, 20
loons, 24
lories, 24
lorises, 25
lungfishes, 23
lyrebirds, 25

macaques, 25
macaws, 24
maggots, 20
magpies, 25
mammals, 25
mammoths, 25
mantids, 20
mantis-shrimps, 19
marmosets, 25
marmots, 25
marsupials, 25
mastodons, 25
mayflies, 20
meal-worms, 20
mealy-bugs, 20
medusae, 6, 11
megapodes, 24
men, 25
mice, 25
    pocket-mice, 25
microscorpions, 18
microsporidians, 10
midges, 20
millepores, 11
millers, 20
millipedes, 19
minks, 25
mites, 18
mockingbirds, 25
mole-crickets, 20
mollusks, 7, 15
monkeys, 25
monotremes, 25
mosquitoes, 20
mosquito-hawks, 20
moss-animals, 7, 15
moths, 20
motmots, 24
mouse-birds, 24
murres, 24
musk-oxen, 25
muskrats, 25
mussels, 16

nautilus, 16
nemas, 14

nematodes, 14
newts, 23
night-crawlers, 17
nudibranchs, 16
nuthatches, 25

octopuses, 16
oil-birds, 24
oligochaetes, 17
opalinids, 10
opossums, 25
opossum-shrimps, 19
orangutans, 25
orioles, 25
orl-flies, 20
ospreys, 24
ostriches, 23
otters, 25
ovenbirds, 25
owls, 24
oyster-catchers, 24
oysters, 16

pacas, 25
pandas, 25
pangolins, 25
parakeets, 24
parrots, 24
peacocks, 24
pearly-nautilus, 16
peccaries, 25
pelecypods, 16
pelicans, 24
penguins, 23
petrels, 24
phalangers, 25
phalaropes, 24
pheasants, 24
phoronids, 15
phyllopoda, 18
piculets, 24
pigeons, 24
pigs, 25
pikas, 25
pillbugs, 19
placentals, 25
plainwanderers, 24
planarians, 12
plantain-eaters, 24
platypus, 25
plovers, 24
pocket-mice, 25
polychaetes, 17
polyclads, 12
porcupines, 25
porpoises, 25
potoos, 24
praying-mantis, 20
prawns, 19

proboscis-worms, 6, 13
pronghorns, 25
proturans, 20
pseudoscorpions, 18
psocids, 20
psyllids, 20
pteropods, 16
puffbirds, 24
punkies, 20

Quails, 24

rabbit-fishes, 23
rabbits, 25
raccoons, 25
radiolarians, 9
rails, 24
ramshorns, 16
ratfishes, 23
rats, 25
    kangaroo-rats, 25
ray-finned fishes, 23
rays, 23
reptiles, 23
rheas, 24
rhinoceroses, 25
rhizopods, 9
ribbon-worms, 6, 13
roaches, 20
roadrunners, 24
rock-jumpers, 20
rollers, 24
rotifers, 6, 13
round-worms, 6, 14

Salamanders, 23
salmon-flies, 20
sand-dollars, 21, 22
sandgrouse, 24
sandpipers, 24
sand-stars, 21
sandworms, 17
sawflies, 21
scale-insects, 20
scuds, 19
scorpion-flies, 20
scorpions, 18
    book-scorpions, 18
    false-scorpions, 18
    microscorpions, 18
    pseudoscorpions, 18
    tailless-whip-scorpions, 18
    whip-scorpions, 18
scorpion-spiders, 55
screamers, 24
sea-anemones, 6, 11
sea-cows, 25

sea-cucumbers, 22
sea-fans, 11
sea-feathers, 11
sea-hares, 15
sea-lilies, 21
sea-lions, 25
sea-urchins, 21
seals, 25
sea-mats, 15
sea-mosses, 15
sea-pansies, 11
sea-pens, 11
sea-spiders, 17
sea-squirts, 7, 22
sea-stars, 21
sea-walnuts, 6, 12
secretary-birds, 24
segmented-worms, 7, 16
serpent-flies, 20
serpent-stars, 21
sharks, 23
shearwaters, 24
sheep, 25
shells
    boat-shells, 16
    butterfly-shells, 16
    ear-shells, 15
    lamp-shells, 7, 15
    tooth-shells, 16
    tusk-shells, 16
shrews, 25
    tree-shrews, 25
shrikes, 25
shrimps, 19
    brine-shrimps, 18
    fairy-shrimps, 18
    mantis-shrimps, 19
    opossum-shrimps, 19
silicoflagellates, 9
silver-fish, 20
siphonophores, 11
sipunculid worms, 16
skates, 23
skimmers, 24
skippers, 20
skunks, 25
slime-eels, 23
slime-molds, 9
sloths, 25
slugs, 15, 16
snails, 15
    land-snails, 16
snakebirds, 24
snake-doctors, 20
snake-flies, 20
snakes, 23
snipe, 24
snow-fleas, 20
soft-corals, 11
solitaires, 24
solpugids, 18

songbirds, 25
soothsayers, 20
sowbugs, 19
spiders, 18
    black-widows, 18
    scorpion-spiders, 55
    sea-spiders, 17
    sun-spiders, 18
spiny-headed-worms, 6, 13
spittle-bugs, 20
sponges, 6, 10
    calcareous sponges, 10
    chalky sponges, 10
    glass-sponges, 10
    horny-sponges, 10
    stone-sponges, 10
spoonbills, 24
springtails, 20
squids, 16
squirrels, 25
starfishes, 21
starlings, 25
stick-insects, 20
stilts, 24
stony-corals, 11
stone-flies, 20
stone-sponges, 10
storks, 24
stromatoporoids, 31
stylopids, 21
sucking lice, 20
sun-animalcules, 9
sunbitterns, 24
sungrebes, 24
sun-spiders, 18
surf-birds, 24
swallows, 25
swans, 24
swifts, 24

tailless-whip-scorpions, 18
tanagers, 25
tapeworms, 12
tapirs, 25
tarantula-hawks, 21
tarantulas, 18
tarsiers, 25
Tasmanian-wolf, 25
tenrecs, 25
termites, 20
terns, 24
thrashers, 25
thread-worms, 6, 14
thrips, 20
thorny-corals, 12
thrushes, 25
ticks, 18
tinamous, 24
tintinnids, 10
titmice, 25

toads, 23
todies, 24
tongue-worms, 22
tooth-shells, 16
tortoises, 23
toucans, 24
touracos, 24
tree-hoppers, 20
tree-shrews, 25
triclads, 12
trogans, 24
tropicbirds, 24
trout-flies, 20
trumpeters, 24
tubeworms, 17
tunicates, 22
turbans, 15
turkeys, 24
turnstones, 24
turtles, 23
tusk-shells, 16

Urchins
    cake-urchins, 22
    heart-urchins, 21, 22
    sea-urchins, 21

Vampires, 25
velvet-ants, 21
vertebrates, 7, 23
vireos, 25

voles, 25
vultures, 24

Wagtails, 25
walking-sticks, 20
walruses, 25
warblers, 25
wasps, 21
    gall-wasps, 21
    tarantula-hawks, 21
    wood-wasps, 20
water-bears, 7, 17
water-fleas, 18
water-pennies, 20
wattlebirds, 25
waxwings, 25
webspinners, 20
weasels, 25
weaverbirds, 25
weevils, 20
whales, 25
wheel-animalcules, 6, 13
whip-scorpions, 18
white-ants, 20
white-flies, 20
white-grubs, 20
wire-worms, 20
wolverines, 25
wolves, 25
woodcock, 24
woodhewers, 25
woodpeckers, 24

wood-wasps, 21
woolly-bears, 20
worms
    acorn-worms, 22
    angle-worms, 17
    arrow-worms, 7, 21
    beard-worms, 7, 21
    earthworms, 17
    flatworms, 6, 12
    glow-worms, 20
    gordian-worms, 7, 14
    horsehair-worms, 7, 14
    meal-worms, 20
    proboscis-worms, 6, 13
    ribbon-worms, 6, 13
    round-worms, 6, 14
    segmented-worms, 7,
      16
    spiny-headed-worms,
      6, 13
    sandworms, 17
    sipunculid worms, 16
    tapeworms, 12
    thread-worms, 6, 14
    tongue-worms, 22
    tubeworms, 17
    wire-worms, 20
wrens, 25
wrentits, 25

Zebras, 25
zorapterans, 20

# INDEX TO LATIN NAMES

Acalephae, 44
Acantharia, 40
Acanthaspida
    Graptozoa, 42
    Vertebrata, 64
Acanthaspidomorpha, 64
Acanthinocyathida, 42
Acanthistida, 42
Acanthobdellida, 17, 52
Acanthobdelliformes, 52
Acanthocephala, 6, 13, 36,
    46
Acanthocyatha, 42
Acanthodiformes, 64
Acanthodii, 64
Acanthodioidea, 64
Acanthoessi, 64
Acanthoessiformes, 64
Acanthoglossa, 64
Acanthometrida, 40
Acanthophractida, 40
Acanthopterygii, 66
Acanthothoraci, 64
Acari, 54
Acarida, 18, 54
Acarina, 54
Accipitres, 69
Accipitriformes, 69
Acephala, 50
Acerata, 53
Acetabulifera, 50
Acineta, 41
Acinetaria, 41
Acipenseriformes, 65
Acipenseroidea, 65
Acnidaria, 36, 44
Acnidosporidia, 40
Acochlidiacea, 50
Acoela
    Mollusca, 16, 50
    Platyhelminthes, 12,
        45
Acoelomata, 6, 36
Acopa, 63
Acrania, 37, 63
Acrasiae, 40
Acraspeda, 44
Acrosauria, 67
Acrothoracica, 18, 56
Actinanthida, 44
Actiniaria, 11, 44
Actiniidea, 44
Actinistia, 66

Actinoceroida, 51
Actinoidea
    Coelenterata, 44
    Echinodermata, 60
Actinomyxidia, 9, 40
Actinophrydea, 40
Actinopoda
    Echinodermata, 62
    Protozoa, 9, 40
Actinopterygii, 23, 65
Actinozoa, 44
Actipylaea, 40
Aculifera, 49
Acystosporidia, 40
Adapedonta, 51
Adeleida, 41
Adelochorda, 29
Adelospondyli, 66
Adenopoda, 58
Adinida, 39
Adunata, 60
Aegophiurida, 61
Aepyornithes, 68
Aepyornithiformes, 68
Aeroplanoptera, 58
Aeropneusta, 54
Aetheodontiformes, 65
Aetioptera, 58
Aganasterida, 21, 61
Agelacrinoidea, 61
Aglaspida, 54
Aglossa, 50
Agnatha
    Arthropoda, 58
    Vertebrata, 23, 64
Agnathes, 59
Agnostida, 54
Agnotozoa, 6, 36
Aistopoda, 66
Ajacicyathida, 42
Alcedines, 69
Alciformes, 69
Alcyonacea, 11, 44
Alcyonaria, 11, 44
Alectoromorphae, 68
Alloeocoela, 12, 45
Allogromidiaceae, 40
Alloiocoela, 45
Allotheria, 69
Allotriognathoidea, 66
Amaurochaetaceae, 40
Amaurochaetineae, 40
Amaurosporales, 40

Amblydactyla, 70
Amblypoda, 71
Amblypygi, 55
Ambonodonta, 50
Ambulatoria, 58
Amiiformes, 65
Amioidea, 65
Ammonitida, 51
Ammonitoidea, 50
Amniota, 64
Amoebaea, 40
Amoebina, 40
Amoebogeniae, 40
Amoebosporidia, 40
Amoebozoa, 9, 40
Amphiaspiformes, 64
Amphibia, 23, 66
Amphibioidea, 66
Amphicoela, 67
Amphidiscophora, 41
Amphigastropoda, 49
Amphilinidea, 12, 46
Amphimorphae, 69
Amphineura, 15, 49
Amphioxi, 23, 63
Amphipoda, 19, 56
Amphirhina, 64
Amphirhyncha, 64
Amphoridea, 60
Anacanthoidea, 66
Anamerentoma, 57
Anamnia, 64
Anamorpha, 57
Anapsida, 23, 67
Anarthrodira, 64
Anaspida, 64
Anaspidacea, 19, 56
Anaspidea, 50
Anaspides, 56
Anaspidoidea, 64
Anatinacea, 50
Ancylopoda, 70
Ancyrotricha, 19, 57
Androgyna, 49
Anemineae, 40
Anguilliformes, 66
Anguilluloidea, 47
Angusticoela, 67
Animalia, 6, 36
Anisaxia, 58
Anisomyaria, 50
Anisopleura, 49
Anisopoda, 56

Anisoptera, 58
Annelida, 7, 16, 37, 52
Annulata, 37, 52
Anoecia, 43
Anomalobranchia, 51
Anomalodesmacea, 51
Anomalodesmata, 51
Anomocoela, 67
Anomodontia, 68
Anomomeristica, 52
Anomostraca, 56
Anomura, 56
Anopla, 46
Anoplura, 20, 59
Anostraca, 18, 55
Anseres, 24, 69
Anseriformes, 24, 69
Antennata, 53
Anthocyatha, 42
Anthomedusae, 43
Anthomorphida, 42
Anthozoa, 11, 44
Anthozoariae, 44
Anthracomarti, 54
Anthracomartida, 54
Anthracomorphoidea, 67
Anthracosauria, 67
Anthracosauroidea, 67
Anthropoidea, 70
Antiarchi, 64
Antiarchoidea, 64
Anticorallia, 44
Antipatharia, 12, 44
Antipathidea, 44
Antliata, 59
Anura, 23, 66
Aphacellae, 43
Aphaneura, 52
Aphaniptera, 59
Aphasmidia, 47
Aphelophlebia, 58
Aphetohyoidea, 64
Aphrothoraca, 40
Aphylles, 45
Aplacophora, 15, 49
Aplocoela, 36, 46
Aplosporidia, 40
Aplysiacea, 50
Apoda
    Amphibia, 23, 66
    Arthropoda, 19, 56
    Aves, 24, 69
    Echinodermata, 22, 62
Apodes, 66
Apodiformes, 69
Apodoidea, 66
Apomatostoma, 50
Aporhabdina, 41
Aporidea, 12, 46
Aporita, 60

Apostomina, 41
Appendicularia, 63
Apsidospondyli, 67
Aptera, 57
Apterygea, 24, 68
Apterygiformes, 24, 68
Apterygogenea, 57
Apterygota, 20, 57
Apygia, 49
Arachnida, 18, 54
Arachnoidea, 54
Arachnomorpha, 53
Araeolaimoidea, 14, 47
Araeoscelida, 67
Araneae, 18, 55
Araneida, 8, 55
Archaehymenoptera, 58
Archaeoceti, 70
Archaeocopida, 55
Archaeocyatha, 36, 42
Archaeogastropoda, 15, 49
Archaeophyllida, 42
Archaeopteryges, 68
Archaeopterygiformes, 68
Archaeornithes, 68
Archaeostraca, 55
Archiacanthocephala, 13, 46
Archiannelida, 17, 52
Archichaetopoda, 52
Archinacelloidea, 49
Archipolypoda, 57
Archipterygota, 58
Architarbi, 54
Architarbida, 54
Architeuthacea, 51
Archodonata, 57
Archonta, 70
Archosauria, 67
Archosauromorpha, 67
Arctolepiformes, 64
Arcyriaceae, 40
Armadillomorpha, 57
Arthrocephala, 53
Arthrodira, 64
Arthrodiroidea, 64
Arthropleurida, 53
Arthropoda, 7, 17, 37, 53
Arthropomata, 49
Arthrostraca, 56
Arthrotardigrada, 17, 52
Articulata
    Brachiopoda, 15, 49
    Coelomata, 27
    Echinodermata, 21, 60
Artiodactyla, 25, 71
Ascaroidea, 14, 48
Aschelminthes, 28
Ascidiacea, 22, 63
Ascidiastella, 62
Asclerocorallia, 44

Ascoceroida, 51
Asconosa, 41
Ascorhynchomorpha, 54
Ascospermophora, 19, 57
Ascothoracica, 19, 56
Aseptata, 44
Asiphonida, 50
Aspidobothria, 45
Aspidobranchiata, 49
Aspidocephali, 64
Aspidochirota, 22, 62
Aspidochirotida, 62
Aspidocotylea, 45
Aspidogastrea, 12, 45
Aspidorhynchiformes, 65
Aspidorhynchoidea, 65
Aspidospondyli, 67
Aspiraculata, 22, 63
Aspirigera, 41
Aspirotricha, 41
Aspirotrichaceae, 41
Asplanchnaceae, 47
Asteroidea, 21, 61
Asterolepiformes, 64
Asterozoa, 60
Asthenodonta, 51
Asthenodontida, 50
Astomata, 41
Astomina, 41
Astrapotheria, 71
Astraspiformes, 64
Astromonaxonellida, 42
Astrophora, 42
Astrorhizidea, 40
Ateleopiformes, 66
Ateleopoidea, 66
Atelostomata, 62
Atentaculata, 45
Athecanephria, 21, 60
Athecata, 43
Atomiosoma, 46
Atremata
    Brachiopoda, 15, 49
    Tunicata, 63
Aulodonta, 62
Auluroidea, 61
Autobranchiata, 50
Autoscolecida, 36
Aves, 23, 68
Axifera, 44
Azygobranchia, 50

Babesiida, 41
Balanoglossida, 22, 63
Barrandeoceratida, 51
Barypoda, 71
Barytheria, 70
Basommatophora, 16, 50
Bassleroceratida, 51
Bathyclupeiformes, 66

Bathyclupeoidea, 66
Bathyuriscidea, 54
Batoidea, 23, 65
Batrachia, 23, 66
Batrachoidea, 66
Batrachoidiformes, 66
Batrachosauria, 67
Bdellacea, 13, 46
Bdelloidaceae, 46
Bdelloidea, 13, 46
Bdellomorpha, 46
Bdellonemertea, 13, 46
Belemnoida, 51
Bellerophontacea, 49
Beloniformes, 66
Beroida, 12, 45
Beryciformes, 66
Berycomorphoidea, 66
Beyrichiida, 55
Bilateria, 27
Biporophyllidea, 12, 46
Birkeniiformes, 64
Bivalvia, 16, 50
Blastoidea, 60
Blattaeformia, 58
Blattaria, 20, 58
Blattoidea, 58
Bobasatraniiformes, 65
Bolinopsidea, 45
Bothriocephaloidea, 46
Bothriocidaroida, 62
Bothriocidaroidea, 62
Botryoidea, 40
Brachiata
    Echinodermata, 60
    Pogonophora, 37, 59
Brachionocephala, 48
Brachionoidea, 47
Brachionopoda, 48
Brachiopoda, 7, 15, 37, 49
Brachyopterygii, 65
Brachythoraci, 64
Brachyura, 56
Bradorina, 55
Bradyodonti, 65
Bradyodontoidea, 65
Branchiata, 53
Branchionobranchia, 48
Branchiopoda
    Brachiopoda, 48
    Crustacea, 18, 55
Branchiostomoidea, 63
Branchiotremata, 29
Branchiura, 18, 56
Breyeridea, 58
Brooksellida, 43
Bruta, 70
Bryozoa, 7, 15, 37, 48
Bucerotes, 69
Bullomorpha, 50
Bunodomorpha, 54

Bunotheria, 70
Burgessiida, 53


Caducichordata, 63
Caecilia, 66
Caenagnathae, 68
Caenagnathiformes, 68
Caenogastropoda, 15, 50
Caenolestoidea, 70
Calanoida, 18, 55
Calcarea, 10, 41
Calcarineae, 40
Calcispongea, 10, 41
Caligoida, 18, 56
Calonemineae, 40
Caloneurodea, 58
Calopteriformes, 65
Calycophora, 43
Calycozoa, 44
Calyptoblastea, 43
Calyssozoa, 6, 14, 36, 48
Camallanta, 48
Camarodonta, 62
Camaroidea, 43
Camarostomata, 55
Cambridioidea, 49
Camerata, 60
Campanulariae, 43
Campodeoidea, 57
Canaliculata, 61
Caprimulgi, 24, 69
Caprimulgiformes, 24, 69
Carinatae, 68
Carnivora, 25, 70
Carnivores, 70
Carnosida, 10, 42
Carpoidea, 61
Carybdeida, 44
Caryophyllacea, 45
Caryophyllidea, 12, 46
Cassiduloida, 22, 62
Casuarii, 24, 68
Casuariiformes, 24, 68
Capitelliformia, 52
Catenata, 39, 42
Catenulida, 45
Cathartidiformes, 69
Caudata, 66
Caulogastra, 18, 54
Cecomorphae, 68
Centrechinoida, 21, 62
Centroceratida, 51
Centrohelidia, 40
Cephalacanthoidea, 66
Cephalaspida, 64
Cephalaspidea, 50
Cephalaspidiformes, 64
Cephalaspidomorpha, 23, 64
Cephalobaenida, 17, 53

Cephalocarida, 18, 55
Cephalochordata, 7, 23, 37, 63
Cephalodiscidea, 22, 62
Cephalophora, 48
Cephalopoda, 16, 50
Cephalostigmata, 19, 57
Cephaloxeniformes, 65
Ceratiocarina, 56
Ceratiomyxaceae, 40
Ceratocarina, 56
Ceratodonti, 66
Ceratodontiformes, 67
Ceratophora, 37, 52
Ceratosa, 41
Ceratosida, 41
Ceratospongida, 41
Ceriantharia, 12, 45
Cerianthiae, 45
Cerianthidea, 45
Ceriantipatharia, 12, 45
Cestida, 12, 45
Cestoda, 12, 45
Cestodaria, 12, 46
Cestoidea
    Ctenophora, 45
    Platyhelminthes, 45
Cetacea, 25, 70
Cete, 70
Chaetetida, 44
Chaetodermatida, 15, 49
Chaetodermomorpha, 49
Chaetognatha, 7, 21, 37, 59
Chaetonotidea, 13, 47
Chaetonotoidea, 13, 47
Chaetopoda, 17, 52
Chaetosomatida, 47
Chalarothoraca, 40
Chalicotheria, 70
Charadriae, 24, 69
Charadriiformes, 24, 69
Charybdeida, 44
Chaudhuriiformes, 66
Chaudhurioidea, 66
Cheiloctenostoma, 48
Cheilostomata, 15, 48
Cheilostomellaceae, 40
Cheiracanthiformes, 64
Cheiropterygia, 64
Cheleutoptera, 58
Chelicerata, 52
Chelifera, 56
Chelonethida, 54
Chelonia, 23, 67
Cheloniellida, 53
Chenomorphae, 69
Chernetes, 54
Chernetidea, 54
Chilognatha, 19, 57
Chilophiurida, 21, 62
Chilopoda, 19, 57

Chilostomata, 48
Chilostomellidea, 40
Chimaerae, 23, 65
Chimaeriformes, 65
Chimaeroidea, 65
Chiroptera, 25, 70
Chitonida, 49
Chlamydomonadina, 39
Chlamydophora, 40
Chloromonadaceae, 39
Chloromonadina, 9, 39
Choanichthyes, 23, 66
Choanoflagellata, 39
Chondrenchelyes, 65
Chondrenchelyiformes, 65
Chondrichthyes, 23, 65
Chondrophora, 43
Chondropterygii, 65
Chondrostei, 23, 65
Chondrosteoidea, 65
Chonotricha, 10, 41
Chordata, 30
Choristida, 10, 42
Chromadoroidea, 14, 47
Chromomonadina, 39
Chrysomonadaceae, 39
Chrysomonadina, 9, 39
Ciconiae, 24, 69
Ciconiiformes, 24, 69
Cidaroida, 21, 62
Ciliata, 10, 41
Ciliatoidea, 41
Cilioflagellata, 39
Ciliophora, 39
Cirrhobranchiata, 50
Cirrhostomi, 37, 63
Cirrigrada, 61
Cirripedia, 18, 56
Cladida, 60
Cladistia, 65
Cladistioidea, 65
Cladocera, 18, 55
Cladocopa
    Arthropoda, 55
    Mollusca, 50
Cladodontiformes, 65
Cladoidea, 60
Cladophiurae, 61
Cladoselachiformes, 65
Cladoselachii, 65
Cladoselachoidea, 65
Climatiiformes, 64
Clistenterata, 49
Clitellata, 52
Clupeiformes, 66
Clypeastroida, 22, 62
Cnemidolestoidea, 59
Cnidaria, 6, 11, 36, 43
Cnidosporidia, 9, 40
Coadunata, 60
Coccidia, **9, 40**

Coccidiomorpha, 40
Coccolithophorida, 9, 39
Coccostei, 64
Coccosteiformes, 64
Coccosteomorphi, 64
Coccyges, 69
Cochlides, 49
Cochliostraca, 49
Coelacanthiformes, 66
Coelacanthini, 66
Coelenterata, 6, 11, 36, 43
Coelhelminthes, 37, 52
Coelolepida, 64
Coelolepidoidea, 64
Coelolepiformes, 64
Coelomata, 7, 37
Coenothecalia, 11, 44
Coleoidea, 50
Coleoptera, 20, 59
Coleopteroidea, 58
Colii, 24, 69
Coliiformes, 24, 69
Collaria, 36, 44
Collembola, 20, 58
Colloconchida, 50
Collodaria, 40
Collothecacea, 13, 47
Colobognatha, 19, 57
Colopyga, 55
Colossendeomorpha, 54
Columbae, 24, 69
Columbiformes, 24, 69
Colymbae, 24, 68
Colymbiformes, 24, 68
Colymbomorphae, 68
Comatulida, 21, 61
Compsognatha, 68
Conchifera, 50
Conchophora, 50
Conchorhaga, 47
Conchostraca, 18, 55
Condylarthra, 70
Conoclypina, 62
Conocoryphida, 54
Conodonta, 64
Conodontophorida, 64
Conularida, 36, 43
Conulariida, 43
Conulata, 43
Copelata, 63
Copeognatha, 59
Copepoda, 18, 55
Coraciae, 24, 69
Coraciiformes, 24, 69
Coraciomorphae, 68
Coralla, **44**
Corallaria, 44
Coralligena, **44**
Corallimorpharia, 11, 44
Cornacuspongia, **41**
Corona, 44

Coronata, **60**
Coronatae, 11, 44
Coronatida, 44
Corrodentia, 20, 59
Corticata, 39
Corynexochida, 54
Coryphodontia, 70
Costata, 60
Cotylosauria, 67
Craniata, 37, 64
Craspedomonadina, 39
Craterostigma, 19, 57
Creodonta, 70
Crepipoda, 49
Crinoidea, 21, 60
Crocodilia, 23, 67
Crossopterygii, 23, 66
Crossopterygioidea, 66
Crustacea, 18, 55
Cryptocephala, 52
Cryptocoela
    Trematoda, 45
    Turbellaria, 45
Cryptodonata, 58
Cryptodonta, 51
Cryptodontia, 58
Cryptomonadaceae, 39
Cryptomonadina, 9, 39
Cryptoparamera, 44
Cryptostigmata, 55
Cryptostomata, 48
Cryptozonia, 61
Crypturi, 24, 68
Crypturiformes, 24, 68
Ctenarea, 36, 44
Ctenobranchiata, 50
Ctenodipterini, 66
Ctenodontiformes, 67
Ctenophora, 6, 12, 36, 45
Ctenophoraria, 36, 44
Ctenoplanidea, 45
Ctenostomata, 15, 48
Ctenostomina, 41
Cubomedusae, 11, 44
Cuculi, 24, 69
Cuculiformes, 24, 69
Cucullifera, 55
Cucumariida, 62
Cumacea, 19, 56
Cursoria, 58
Cyamoidea, 61
Cyathaspiformes, 64
Cyathocrinacea, 61
Cyathospongia, 36, 42
Cyclicozoa, 44
Cyclobranchia, 49
Cyclocorallia, 44
Cyclodonta, 51
Cycloidea, 61
Cyclomyaria, 22, 63
Cyclophyllidea, 12, 46

Cyclopoida, 18, 55
Cyclorhaga, 47
Cyclostomata
    Bryozoa, 15, 48
    Vertebrata, 23, 64
Cydippida, 12, 45
Cynostraca, 49
Cypriniformes, 66
Cyprinodontiformes, 66
Cyprinodontoidea, 66
Cyrtellaria, 40
Cyrtochoanites, 51
Cyrtocrinida, 21, 60
Cyrtoidea, 40
Cystasteroidea, 61
Cystechinoidea, 60
Cystica, 45
Cystidea, 60
Cystocidaroidea, 60
Cystocrinoidea, 60
Cystoflagellata, 39
Cystoidea, 60
Cytoidea, 39
Cytomorpha, 39
Cytophora, 40
Cytosporidia, 40

Dacnostomata, 58
Dactylifera, 45
Dactylopteriformes, 66
Daubentomioidea, 70
Decabrachia, 50
Decapoda
    Arthropoda, 19, 56
    Mollusca, 16, 50
Decembrachiata, 50
Deinocephalia, 68
Delobranchia, 54
Demospongea, 10, 41
Dendroceratina, 41
Dendrochirozoa, 22, 62
Dendrochirotida, 62
Dendroidea, 43
Deratoptera, 58
Dermaptera, 20, 58
Dermodermaptera, 58
Dermoptera, 25, 70
Desmodonta, 51
Desmomyaria, 22, 63
Desmophora, 41
Desmoscolecoidea, 14, 47
Desmospongea, 41
Desmothoraca, 40
Diadecta, 67
Diadectomorpha, 67
Diadematoida, 62
Diademoida, 62
Dialytina, 41
Diantennata, 53
Diaphanopteroidea, 58

Diapsida, 23, 67
Diatrymae, 69
Diatrymiformes, 69
Dibothridiata, 46
Dibranchiata, 16, 50
Dicellura, 57
Dicestoda, 46
Dichoporita, 60
Dickinsoniida, 43
Dicoelia, 44
Dictyida, 41
Dictyobranchia, 63
Dictyoceratina, 41
Dictyonina, 10, 41
Dictyoptera, 58
Dictyosteliaceae, 40
Dicyclica, 61
Dicyemida, 11, 42
Dicynodontia, 68
Didelphia, 70
Didymiaceae, 40
Digenea, 12, 45
Digenetica, 45
Digononta, 46
Diktyobranchia, 63
Dimyaria
    Mollusca, 50
    Rhynchocoela, 46
Diniferidea, 39
Dinocerata, 71
Dinoflagellata, 9, 39
Dinophilea, 52
Dinornithes, 68
Dinornithiformes, 68
Dinosauria, 67
Dioctophymoidea, 14, 48
Diogenodonta, 51
Diotocardia, 49
Diphyllidea, 45
Diplarthra, 70
Diplasiocoela, 67
Dipleurozoa, 43
Diplobathra, 60
Diplobathrida, 60
Diplodonti, 65
Diplodontiformes, 65
Diploglossata, 58
Diplomorpha, 43
Diplopoda, 19, 57
Diploporita, 60
Diplostraca, 55
Diplura, 57
Dipneumona, 66
Dipneusti, 66
Dipnoa, 67
Dipnoi, 23, 66
Diprotodontia, 70
Diptera, 20, 59
Dipteri, 66
Dipteriformes, 66
Discinocarina, 55

Discocephalioidea, 66
Discomedusae, 44
Discophora, 44
Discosoroida, 51
Disculicepitidea, 12, 45
Disparata, 60
Disparida, 60
Distomea, 45
Docoglossa, 49
Dodecacorallia, 44
Doliolida, 63
Dorylaimoidea, 14, 47
Dorypteriformes, 65
Dracunculoidea, 14, 48
Dromeognathae, 68
Dromosauria, 68
Duplicidentata, 70
Dysodonta, 51

Ecardines, 49
Ecaudata, 66
Echeniiformes, 66
Echiniiformes, 66
Echiniscoidea, 17, 52
Echinocystida, 40
Echinocystoida, 62
Echinoidea, 21, 62
Echinodera, 6, 13, 36, 47
Echinodermata, 7, 21, 37, 60
Echinozoa, 60
Echiurida, 16, 51
Echiuroidea, 7, 16, 37, 51
Echiuroina, 16, 51
Ectobranchiata, 62
Ectocarpen, 43
Ectognatha, 57
Ectoparasitica, 45
Ectoprocta, 7, 37, 48
Ectospora, 40
Ectotrophi, 57
Edentata, 25, 70
Edentates, 70
Edestidi, 65
Edrioasteroidea, 61
Edriophthalma, 56
Edwardsiidea, 44
Eimeriida, 41
Elasipoda, 22, 62
Elasipodida, 62
Elasmobranchii, 23, 65
Ellesmeroceroida, 51
Eleutherata, 59
Eleutheroblastea, 43
Eleutherorhabda, 50
Eleutherozoa, 60
Ellipoptera, 58
Ellipura, 57
Elytroptera, 59
Embiidina, 58

Embioidea, 58
Embioptera, 20, 58
Embolobranchiata, 54
Embolomeri, 66
Embrithopoda, 71
Emeraldellida, 53
Emmenognatha, 59
Emydosauria, 67
Encrinasteriae, 61
Endeiolepiformes, 64
Endoaria, 44
Endobranchiata, 62
Endoceroida, 51
Endocyclica, 62
Endoprocta, 6, 14, 36, 48
Endopterygota, 20, 59
Endospora, 40
Endosporeae, 40
Enopla, 46
Enoplata, 47
Enoploidea, 14, 47
Enterocoela, 6, 27, 36
Enterogona, 63
Enteropneusta, 7, 22, 37, 63
Enterozoa, 27, 36
Entodiniomorphina, 41
Entognatha, 57
Entomocrania, 37, 63
Entomostraca, 55
Entoprocta, 14, 36, 48
Entotrophi, 20, 57
Eoacanthocephala, 13, 46
Eoanura, 66
Eocrinoidea, 61
Eodiscida, 54
Eopaleodictyoptera, 58
Eoplacophora, 49
Eosuchia, 67
Eotetrapoda, 64
Eozoa, 6, 36, 39
Epectinata, 54
Ephemerida, 20, 58
Ephemeroidea, 58
Ephemeroptera, 58
Epimorpha, 57
Epiparia, 54
Epipolasida, 10, 42
Eplacentalia, 69
Erpobdellida, 52
Errantia, 17, 52
Eterocotylea, 45
Euamphibia, 67
Euanostraca, 55
Euanura, 66
Eu-arachnida, 54
Euarthrodira, 64
Euarthropoda, 37, 52
Euasteriae, 61
Eublastoidea, 60
Eubleptidodea, 57
Eubradyodonti, 65

Eucarida, 56
Euceratosa, 41
Eucestoda, 45
Euchorda, 37, 64
Euciliata, 10, 41
Eucirripedia, 56
Eucoelomata, 37
Eucopepoda, 18, 55
Eucrinoidea, 60
Eucrustacea, 55
Eucystoidea, 60
Eudesmodontida, 50
Euechinoidea, 62
Euentomata, 57
Euflagellata, 39
Euglenaceae, 39
Euglenida, 39
Euglenoidina, 9, 39
Eugnatha, 57
Eugregarinida, 41
Eulamellibranchia, 16, 50
Eumalacostraca, 56
Eumetazoa, 36
Eumycetozoa, 40
Eunotosauria, 67
Euonychophora, 17, 53
Euornithes, 68
Eupantopoda, 17, 54
Euphaneroidea, 64
Euphausiacea, 19, 56
Euphyllopoda, 55
Euplasmodida, 40
Euplexoptera, 58
Eupoliida, 46
Euryalae, 61
Euryalida, 61
Euryapsida, 67
Eurylaemi, 69
Eurypterida, 54
Eurysterna, 57
Eurystomata, 48
Euselachii, 65
Eusuchia, 67
Eutardigrada, 17, 52
Eutaxodonta, 50
Eutheria, 25, 70
Euthyneura, 49
Euxiphosura, 54
Exocyatha, 42
Exocyclica, 62
Exocycloida, 21, 62
Exopterygoptera, 58
Exopterygota, 20, 58
Exosporae, 40
Exosporidia, 41
Extrasiphonata, 51

Falcones, 24, 69
Falconiformes, 24, 69
Ferae, 70

Ferungulata, 70
Filarioidea, 14, 48
Filibranchia, 16, 50
Filosa, 39
Fissipedia, 70
Fistulata, 61
Fistulides, 62
Flagellata, 9, 39
Flexibilia, 60
Flosculariacea, 13, 47
Foraminifera, 9, 40
Forcipulata, 21, 61

Gadiformes, 66
Galaxiiformes, 66
Galeodea, 55
Galeoidei, 65
Galli, 24, 69
Galliformes, 24, 69
Gallinae, 69
Gasterozoa, 49
Ganodonta, 70
Ganoidi, 65
Gasteropoda, 49
Gasteropodophora, 49
Gasterosteiformes, 66
Gasterostoma, 45
Gastornithes, 68
Gastraeopoda, 49
Gastrocaulia, 49
Gastropoda, 15, 49
Gastrotricha, 6, 13, 36, 47
Gaviae, 24, 68
Gaviiformes, 24, 68
Gemuendiniformes, 64
Geophilomorpha, 19, 57
Geophylomorpha, 57
Gigantostraca, 54
Giganturiformes, 66
Giganturoidea, 66
Ginglymodi, 65
Glires, 70
Globidia, 10, 40
Globigerinidea, 40
Glossata, 59
Glosselytrodea, 58
Glossophora, 48
Gnathobdellida, 17, 52
Gnathobdelliformes, 52
Gnathophiurida, 21, 61
Gnathopoda, 54
Gnathostomata
    Echinodermata, 62
    Vertebrata, 64
Gobiesociformes, 66
Goniactinida, 61
Gordiacea, 6, 14, 36, 48
Gordididea, 48
Gordioidea, 14, 36, 48

Gorgonacea, 11, 44
Gradientia, 66
Grallae, 69
Graptoblasti, 42
Graptolithida, 43
Graptoloidea, 43
Graptovermida, 42
Graptozoa, 36, 43
Gregarina, 40
Gregarinida, 9, 40
Gressores, 69
Gressoria, 58
Gromiidea, 40
Grues, 24, 69
Gruiformes, 24, 69
Grylloblattoidea, 20, 58
Guttulinaceae, 40
Gymnamoebaea, 40
Gymnoblastea, 43
Gymnodiniaceae, 39
Gymnolaemata, 15, 48
Gymnomyxa, 39
Gymnonisciformes, 65
Gymnophiona, 23, 66
Gymnosomata, 50
Gymnosporidia, 40
Gymnostomata, 41
Gyracanthiformes, 64
Gyracanthocephala, 46
Gyrocotylidea, 12, 46
Gyrosomata, 50

Hadentomoidea, 59
Hadromerida, 10, 42
Haemacryma, 64
Haematherma, 64
Haemocytozoa, 40
Haemosporidia, 9, 40
Halichondrida, 10, 42
Hallopoda, 68
Halosauriformes, 66
Halterata, 59
Halteriptera, 59
Hapalopteroidea, 59
Haplocrinacea, 61
Haplocyemata, 37, 63
Haplodoci, 66
Haplodrili, 52
Haplosclerida, 10, 42
Haplosporidia, 10, 40
Haplozoa, 60, 61
Haptopoda, 54
Haptopodida, 54
Harpacticoida, 18, 55
Haustellata, 59
Helianthoida, 44
Helicosporidia, 10, 40
Helioflagellida, 40
Heliolitida, 44
Heliornithiformes, 69

Heliozoa, 9, 40
Helminthomorpha, 37, 63
Hemibranchia, 50
Hemichordata, 29
Hemimeroidea, 58
Hemimyaria, 22, 63
Hemiodonata, 58
Hemipodii, 69
Hemipomatostoma, 50
Hemipsocoptera, 59
Hemiptera, 58
Hemizonida, 61
Herocotylida, 45
Herodii, 69
Herodiones, 69
Herpobdellida, 52
Hesperornithes, 68
Hesperornithiformes, 68
Hetairacyathida, 42
Heteractinellida, 41
Heteractinida, 10, 41
Heterocerci, 65
Heterochlorida, 39
Heterocoelida, 41
Heteroconchia, 50
Heterocoralla, 45
Heterocorallia, 44
Heterocotylea, 45
Heterocyemida, 11, 42
Heterodermaceae, 40
Heterodonta, 51
Heterodontida, 50
Heterodontiformes, 65
Heterodontoidea, 65
Heterogangliata, 37, 48
Heterognatha, 19, 56
Heterokaryota, 39
Heteromastigina, 39
Heterometabola, 20, 58
Heteromi, 66
Heteromoidea, 66
Heteromorphae, 69
Heteromya, 50
Heteromyaria, 50
Heteromyota, 16, 51
Heteronemertea, 13, 46
Heterophyllidea, 45
Heteropoda, 50
Heteroptera, 20, 59
Heterosomata, 66
Heterostelea, 60
Heterostigmata, 55
Heterostraci, 64
Heterotardigrada, 17, 52
Heterotricha, 41
Hexaceratina, 41
Hexacorallia, 44
Hexactinellida, 10, 41
Hexactinia, 44
Hexanchiformes, 65
Hexanchoidea, 65

Hexapoda, 20, 57
Hexasterophora, 41
Hippocrepia, 48
Hirudinea, 17, 52
Histosporidia, 40
Histozoa, 6, 36
Holectypoida, 22, 62
Holobranchia, 48
Holocephali, 23, 65
Hologonia, 47
Holomastigina, 39
Holomerentoma, 57
Holometabola, 20, 59
Holopeltidia, 55
Holoptychiformes, 66
Holosiphona, 50
Holostei, 23, 65
Holothurioidea, 22, 62
Holothuroidea, 62
Holotricha, 10, 41
Holotrypasta, 40
Homalopterygia, 37, 59
Homalorhaga, 47
Homalozoa, 60
Homocoelida, 41
Homokaryota, 39
Homomeria, 37, 63
Homomyaria, 50
Homopoda, 53
Homoptera, 20, 59
Homosclerophora, 42
Hoplocarida, 56
Hoplonemertea, 13, 46
Hyalospongea, 10, 41
Hybocrinida, 60
Hydrariae, 43
Hydrida, 43
Hydrocorallinae, 11, 43
Hydroida, 11, 43
Hydromedusae, 43
Hydrophoridea, 60
Hydropneustea, 54
Hydrosauria, 67
Hydrozoa, 11, 43
Hydrozoaria, 43
Hymenocarina, 53
Hymenoptera, 21, 59
Hymenopteroidea, 59
Hymenostomata, 41
Hyparthropoda, 53
Hypermastigina, 9, 39
Hyperoarti, 64
Hyperotreti, 64
Hypoparia, 54
Hypostoma, 60
Hypostomosoidea, 66
Hypotremata, 65
Hypotricha, 41
Hyraces, 71
Hyracoidea, 25, 71

Ichthya, 64
Ichthyocrinacea, 60
Ichthyodorulites, 64
Ichthyopsida, 64
Ichthyopterygia, 67
Ichthyopterygii, 64
Ichthyornes, 68
Ichthyorniformes, 68
Ichthyornithes, 68
Ichthyornithiformes, 68
Ichthyosauria, 67
Ichthyostegalia, 66
Ichthyotomi, 65
Icosteiformes, 66
Icosteioidea, 66
Ictidosauria, 68
Impennes, 68
Inadunata, 60
Inarticulata
    Brachiopoda, 15, 49
    Echinodermata, 60
Inermia, 41
Infusoria, 39
Iniomi, 66
Illoricata, 47
Insecta, 20, 57
Insectivora, 25, 70
Integricephalida, 54
Integripalliata, 51
Intrasiphonata, 51
Irregulares, 60
Irregularia
    Crinoidea, 61
    Echinoidea, 22, 62
Ischnacanthiformes, 64
Isedrolotila, 50
Isocrinida, 21, 60
Isodonta, 51
Isofilibranchia, 50
Isomya, 50
Isoplacophora, 49
Isopleura, 49
Isopoda, 19, 56
Isoptera, 20, 58
Isopygia, 54
Isospondyli, 66
Isospondyloidea, 66
Isuriformes, 65

Jagoriniformes, 65
Juliformia, 57

Kamptozoa, 36, 48
Katapsida, 67
Kathapsida, 67
Keratosida, 10, 41
Kinorhyncha, 6, 13, 36, 47
Krikobranchia, 63

Kustarachne, 55
Kustarachnida, 55

Labechioidea, 43
Labellata, 55
Labidura, 58
Labyrinthodontia, 66
Labyrinthulidea, 39
Lacertilia, 67
Laemodipoda, 56
Laemophiurida, 21, 61
Lagenidea, 40
Lagomorpha, 25, 70
Lamellata, 49
Lamellibranchiata, 16, 50
Lamniformes, 65
Lamnoidea, 65
Lampridiformes, 66
Lamprosporales, 40
Lariformes, 69
Laro-limicolae, 69
Larvacea, 22, 63
Larvata, 61
Larviformia, 61
Lasaniiformes, 64
Lateribranchiata, 50
Laternulacea, 50
Latigastra, 18, 54
Latisterna, 55
Leanchoiliida, 53
Lebetida, 10, 41
Lecanicephala, 12, 45
Lecanicephaloidea, 45
Lemuroidea, 70
Leperditicopida, 55
Leperditiida, 55
Lepidocentroida, 62
Lepidoglossa, 49
Lepidopleurida, 49
Lepidoptera, 20, 59
Lepidosauria, 67
Lepidosireniformes, 67
Lepidostei, 65
Lepidosteoidea, 65
Lepisostei, 65
Lepisosteiformes, 65
Lepospondyli, 23, 66
Leptocardia, 23, 63
Leptolinae, 43
Leptomedusae, 43
Leptophya, 59
Leptostraca, 56
Lernaeopodoida, 18, 56
Leuconosa, 41
Libellulides, 58
Libelluloidea. 58
Liceaceae, 40
Lichacea, 54
Lichida, **54**
Limacomorpha, 19, 57

Limicolae
    Annelida, 52
    Vertebrata, 68
Limulava, 53
Limulavida, 53
Limulida, 54
Linguatulida, 17, 37, 53
Linguatulodea, 53
Lipocephala, 50
Lipodonta, 51
Lipoptera, 59
Lipostraca, 55
Lissoflagellata, 39
Lithistida, 10, 42
Lithobiomorpha, 19, 57
Lithonina, 41
Lithorhizostomeae, 44
Lithorhizostomatida, 44
Litoptera, 70
Lituolidea, 40
Lobata, 12, 45
Lobosa, 39
Loliginacea, 51
Lophiiformes, 66
Lophogastridea, 19, 56
Lophopoda, 15, 48
Lophotricha, 19, 57
Loricata
    Mollusca, 49
    Rotifera, 47
    Vertebrata, 67
Lucernaria, 44
Lucernariidea, 44
Luciae, 63
Lucida, 63
Luganoidiiformes, 65
Lumbricimorpha, 52
Lychniskida, 41
Lychniskophora, 10, 41
Lygogalaceae, 40
Lyomeroidea, 66
Lyopomata, 49
Lysophiurae, 61
Lysophiuroida, 61
Lyssacina, 41
Lyssakina, 10, 41

Machaeridia, 61
Macrochires, 24, 69
Macrochiriformes, 24, 69
Macrociliobranchia, 50
Macrodasyidea, 13, 47
Macrodasyoidea, 13, 47
Macropetalichthyida, 64
Macropharyngea, 45
Macrosterni, 57
Macrostomida, 45
Macrotrachia, 50
Macrura, 56
Macruriformes, 66

Madreporaria, 11, 44
Malacactiniae, 44
Malachichthyes, 66
Malacobothrii, 45
Malacocotylea, 45
Malacopoda, 37, 52
Malacopterygii, 66
Malacostraca, 19, 56
Malacozoa, 37, 48
Mallophaga, 20, 59
Mammalia, 25, 69
Mammifera, 69
Mandibulata, 52
Mantodea, 20, 58
Marellomorpha, 53
Margaritaceae, 40
Marrellida, 53
Marrellomorpha, 53
Marriocarida, 53
Marsipobranchii, 64
Marsupialia
    Coelenterata, 44
    Vertebrata, 25, 70
Mastacembeliformes, 66
Mastacembelioidea, 66
Mastigophora, 9, 39
Mecaptera, 59
Mecoptera, 20, 59
Medamoptera, 59
Megalichthyiformes, 66
Megalopoda, 62
Megaloptera, 59
Meganisoptera, 58
Megasecoptera, 58
Megasecopterida, 58
Megistanes, 68
Melicertida, 47
Melonechinoida, 62
Melonitoida, 62
Menotyphla, 70
Menurae, 69
Meridogastra, 55
Mermithoidea, 14, 47
Merochaeta, 57
Merostomata, 17, 54
Merostomoidea, 53
Merotrypasta, 40
Merozoa, 45
Mesaxonia, 71
Mesacanthiformes, 64
Mesichthyes, 66
Mesogastropoda, 50
Mesonacida, 54
Mesonemertini, 46
Mesoplacophora, 49
Mesosauria, 68
Mesostigmata, 55
Mesosuchia, 67
Mesozoa, 6, 11, 36, 42
Metacanthocephala, 46
Metacyathida, 42

Metanemertini, 46
Metapsida, 67
Metastigmata, 55
Metatheria, 25, 70
Metazoa, 6, 36
Michelinoceroida, 51
Micramphibia, 66
Microciliobranchia, 50
Microcyprini, 66
Micropharyngea, 45
Micropodi, 24, 69
Micropodiformes, 69
Micropygia, 54
Microsauria, 66
Microsclerophora, 42
Microsporidia, 10, 40
Microthelyphonida, 55
Miliolidea, 40
Milleporida, 11, 43
Millericrinida, 60
Mimetasterida, 53
Miocoela, 36, 46
Miomera, 54
Miomoptera, 59
Mionelminthes, 36, 42
Mirientomata, 57
Miskoa, 52
Mixochoanites, 51
Mixotermitoidea, 58
Mollusca, 7, 15, 37, 49
Molpadida, 62
Molpadonia, 22, 62
Monactinellida, 41
Monadidea, 39
Monaxonida, 41
Monhysteroidea, 14, 47
Moniligastres, 52
Monobathra, 60
Monobathrida, 60
Monoblastidea, 11, 42
Monoblastoidea, 11, 42
Monoblastozoa, 6, 11, 36,
    42
Monoceratina, 41
Monocyatha, 42
Monocyathida, 42
Monocyclica
    Coelenterata, 44
    Echinodermata, 60
Monodelphia, 70
Monogenea, 12, 45
Monogenetica, 45
Monogononta, 13, 47
Monomerostomata, 54
Monomya, 50
Monomyaria, 50
Monophyllidea, 45
Monopisthocotylea, 45
Monoplacophora, 15, 49
Monopneumona, 66
**Monopnoa, 67**

Monopylaria, 40
Monorhina, 64
Monorhyncha, 64
Monotocardia, 50
Monotremata, 25, 69
Monozoa, 46
Monstrilloida, 18, 56
Monticuliporoidea, 48
Mormyriformes, 66
Mormyroidea, 66
Moruloidea, 36, 42
Mosasauria, 67
Mugiliformes, 66
Multisolenida, 44
Multituberculata, 69
Musophagi, 68
Mutica, 70
Mutilata, 70
Mycetophorae, 55
Mycetozoa, 9, 40
Myctophiformes, 66
Myelozoa, 37, 63
Mylostomatiformes, 64
Myodocopa, 55
Myodocopida, 18, 55
Myohyracoidea, 70
Myophiurida, 21, 61
Myosomata, 22, 63
Myriapoda, 53
Myrientomata, 57
Mysidacea, 19, 56
Mystacocarida, 18, 55
Mystacoceti, 70
Myxini, 64
Myxiniformes, 64
Myxinoidea, 64
Myxogasteres, 40
Myxomycetes, 40
Myxospongida, 10, 41
Myxosporidia, 9, 40
Myzostoma, 51
Myzostomaria, 51
Myzostomida, 7, 16, 37, 51

Nahecarida, 56
Naiadida, 50
Naidomorpha, 52
Narcaciontiformes, 65
Narcomedusae, 43
Nasselaria, 40
Nautilida, 51
Nautiloidea, 16, 50
Nebaliacea, 19, 56
Nectaspida, 53
Nectonematoidea, 14, 48
Nectridia, 66
Nemata, 36, 47
Nemathelminthes, 28
Nematoda, 6, 14, 36, 47
Nematoidea, 14, 47

Nematomorpha, 6, 14, 36, 48
Nematophora
    Arthropoda, 19, 57
    Coelenterata, 36, 43
Nematozoa, 36, 43
Nemertea, 46
Nemertinea, 6, 13, 36, 46
Nemuraedes, 58
Neoacanthocephala, 46
Neoblattariae, 58
Neocrinoidea, 61
Neogastropoda, 50
Neognathae, 68
Neoloricata, 15, 49
Neomeniida, 15, 49
Neomeniomorpha, 49
Neoptera, 57
Neopterygii, 65
Neornithes, 23, 68
Neosauromorpha, 67
Neoscyphozoa, 44
Neosporidea, 40
Neotaxodonta, 50
Neotremata, 15, 49
Nereidiformia, 52
Neuroptera, 20, 59
Nidulitida, 41
Nippotaeniidea, 12, 46
Nomarthra, 70
Nomomeristica, 52
Non-calcarea, 41
Notacanthiformes, 66
Notaspidea, 50
Nothosauria, 67
Notidanoidea, 65
Notodelphyoida, 18, 56
Notommatoidea, 47
Notoptera, 58
Notostigma, 57
Notostigmata, 55
Notostigmophora, 19, 57
Notostraca, 18, 55
Notoungulata, 71
Nuda
    Ctenophora, 12, 45
    Protozoa, 40
    Vertebrata, 67
Nudibrachiata, 43
Nudibranchiata, 50
Nummulitidea, 40
Nymphonomorpha, 54

Octacnemida, 22, 63
Octactinellida, 41
Octactinia, 44
Octobrachiata, 51
Octocorallia, 44
Octopoda, 16, 51
Octopoida, 51

Odonata, 20, 58
Odontoceti, 70
Odontognathae, 68
Odontolcae, 68
Odontopleurida, 54
Odontormae, 68
Odontota, 58
Oecioa, 44
Oesthelminthes, 37, 59
Olenellida, 54
Oligochaeta, 17, 52
Oligocnemata, 64
Oligoentomata, 58
Oligomeria, 54
Oligoneura, 58
Oligotrichina, 41
Oncidiacea, 50
Oncoceroida, 51
Oncopoda, 29
Oniscomorpha, 19, 57
Onychophora, 7, 17, 37, 53
Onychura, 55
Oothecaria, 58
Opabiniida, 53
Opalinida, 10, 41
Ophidia, 67
Ophiocephaliformes, 66
Ophiocistioidea, 62
Ophiocystia, 62
Ophiocystiida, 21, 61
Ophiocystioidea, 62
Ophiureae, 61
Ophiurida, 61
Ophiuroidea, 21, 61
Opiliones, 18, 54
Opilionidea, 54
Opisthandria, 57
Opisthobranchia, 15, 50
Opisthocoela, 67
Opisthocomi, 69
Opisthocomiformes, 69
Opisthogoneata, 53
Opisthomi, 66
Opisthoparia, 54
Opisthopora, 17, 52
Opisthospermophora, 19, 57
Ornithae, 68
Ornithischia, 68
Ornithodelphia, 69
Ornithopoda, 68
Ornithosauria, 67
Ornithoscelida, 67
Orthida, 48
Orthochoanites, 51
Orthonectida, 11, 42
Orthopoda, 68
Orthoptera, 20, 58
Ornithurae, 68
Osculosida, 40
Ospiiformes, 65
Ostariophysi, 66

Ostariophysoidea, 66
Osteichthyes, 23, 65
Osteolepides, 66
Osteolepidoti, 66
Osteolepiformes, 66
Osteostraci, 64
Osteostracoidea, 64
Ostracoda, 18, 55
Ostracodermi, 64
Ostracopa, 55
Ostracophori, 64
Ostrapoda, 55
Otocardia, 37, 48
Oxyuroidea, 14, 48

Pachycormiformes, 65
Pachycormoidea, 65
Pachyodonta, 51
Pachyodontida, 50
Pachypodes, 67
Paenungulata, 70
Palaeacanthocephala, 13, 46
Palaeanostraca, 53
Palaeobranchia, 50
Palaeocopida, 55
Palaeocoxopleura, 57
Palaeocrinoidea, 60
Palaeodictyoptera, 58
Palaeo-echinoidea, 62
Palaeognathae, 68
Palaeohemiptera, 59
Palaeohymenoptera, 58
Palaeolamellibranchia, 50
Palaeonemertea, 13, 46
Palaeonemertini, 46
Palaeonisciformes, 65
Palaeonisciodea, 65
Palaeopantopoda, 54
Palaeoptera, 57
Palaeopterygii, 65
Palaeospondyliformes, 65
Palaeospondyloidea, 65
Palaeostraca, 54
Palaeotaxodonta, 51
Palaeotremata, 49
Palechinoidea, 62
Paleoconcha, 51
Paleocopa, 55
Paleo-echinoidea, 62
Paleoloricata, 49
Paleomorpha, 57
Paleonemertea, 46
Paleotremata, 49
Palliata, 37, 48
Palliobranchiopoda, 37, 48
Palpigradi, 55
Palpigradida, 18, 55
Pandictyoptera, 58
Panisoptera, 59

Panorpatae, 59
Panorpina, 59
Panorpoidea, 59
Panprotura, 57
Panthysanura, 57
Pantodonta
    Mollusca, 51
    Vertebrata, 71
Pantodontida, 50
Pantopoda, 54
Pantostomatida, 39
Pantotheria, 70
Parablastoidea, 60
Paracephalophora, 49
Paracoleoptera, 59
Paracrinoidea, 61
Paractinopoda, 62
Parafilibranchia, 50
Paramecoptera, 59
Paramera, 44
Paranemata, 45
Paraneuroptera, 58
Paraplecoptera, 59
Parapsida, 67
Parareptilia, 67
Pararthropoda, 29
Parasita, 59
Parastigmata, 55
Parasuchia, 67
Paratheria, 70
Paratrichoptera, 59
Paraxonia, 71
Parazoa, 6, 36
Pareiasauria, 67
Passeres, 25, 69
Passeriformes, 25, 69
Paucituberculata, 70
Pauropoda, 19, 56
Pectinibranchia, 50
Pectobothrii, 45
Pectinifera, 54
Pedata, 62
Pedicellinida, 14, 48
Pediculati, 66
Pediculatiformes, 66
Pediculidea, 59
Pedipalpida, 55
Pegasiformes, 66
Pelagothurida, 63
Pelargiformes, 69
Pelargomorphae, 68
Pelecani, 24, 69
Pelecaniformes, 24, 69
Pelecypoda, 16, 50
Pelicaniformes, 69
Pelmatozoa, 60
Pelycosauria, 68
Penicillata, 57
Pennatulacea, 11, 44
Pentacrinacea, 61
Pentacrinoidea, 61

Pentamerida, 48
Pentastomida, 7, 17, 37, 53
Peracarida, 56
Perciformes, 66
Percomorphoidea, 66
Percopseiformes, 66
Perennichordata, 63
Peridiniaceae, 39
Perielytrodea, 57
Peripatidea, 17, 53
Peripylaria, 40
Perischoechinoida, 62
Perissodactyla, 25, 71
Peritricha, 10, 41
Perlaria, 58
Perlarides, 58
Perleidiformes, 65
Perloidea, 58
Permodictyoptera, 58
Permodonata, 58
Permoneurodia, 57
Peromedusae, 44
Peromela, 66
Petalichthyida, 64
Petalodontes, 65
Petalodontiformes, 65
Petanoptera, 59
Petromyzonoidea, 64
Petromyzontia, 64
Petromyzontiformes, 64
Phacopida, 54
Phaeoconchia, 40
Phaeocystina, 40
Phaeodaria, 40
Phaeogromia, 40
Phaeosphaeria, 40
Phalangida, 18, 54
Phalangiotarbi, 54
Phalansteriina, 39
Phallostethiformes, 66
Phanerocephala, 52
Phaneropleuriformes, 66
Phanerorhynchiformes, 65
Phanerozonia, 21, 61
Pharetronida, 10, 41
Pharyngidea, 16, 51
Pharyngobdellida, 17, 52
Pharyngobdelliformes, 52
Pharyngobranchii, 37, 63
Phasmidia
    Arthropoda, 20, 58
    Nematoda, 47
Phasmoidea, 58
Phlebobranchiata, 22, 63
Phlebolepiformes, 64
Phoenicopteri, 69
Phoenicopteriformes, 69
Pholadacea, 50
Pholidophoriformes, 65
Pholidophoroidea, 65
Pholidopleuriformes, 65

Pholidota
    Amphibia, 67
    Mammalia, 25, 70
Phoronida, 7, 15, 37, 48
Phragmophora, 51
Phryganoidea, 59
Phryneides, 55
Phrynichida, 18, 55
Phrynophiurida, 21, 61
Phthinorhabdina, 41
Phthiraptera, 58
Phylactolaemata, 15, 48
Phyllobothrioidea, 45
Phyllocarida, 56
Phyllolepida, 64
Phyllolepiformes, 64
Phyllopoda, 55
Phylloptera, 58
Phyllorhyncha, 46
Phyllospondyli, 67
Physapida, 59
Physaraceae, 40
Physoclysti, 66
Physophora, 43
Physopoda, 59
Physostomi, 66
Phytoflagellata, 39
Phytomastigina, 9, 39
Phytomastigophorea, 39
Phytomonadina, 9, 39
Phytosauria, 67
Picariae, 68
Pici, 24, 69
Piciformes, 24, 69
Pinnipedia, 70
Piroplasmidea, 41
Pisces, 64
Pithecoidea, 70
Placentalia, 25, 70
Placentaria, 70
Placipennes, 59
Placodermi, 64
Placodontia, 67
Placoidei, 65
Placophora, 49
Plagiaulacoidea, 69
Plagiostomi, 65
Plagiotremata, 67
Planaria, 45
Planctosphaeroidea, 7, 22, 37, 63
Planipennia, 59
Planuloidea, 36, 42
Plasmodiida, 41
Plasmodroma, 39
Plastidozoa, 36, 39
Plathelminthes, 45
Platodes, 36, 45
Platosomia, 65
Platyasterida, 61
Platycopa, 55

Platyctenea, 12, 45
Platydesmiformia, 57
Platyelmia, 45
Platyhelmia, 45
Platyhelminthes, 6, 12, 36, 45
Platymalakia, 49
Platypoda, 50
Platyrhina, 70
Platysiagiformes, 65
Plecoptera, 20, 58
Plectellaria, 40
Plectognathoidea, 66
Plectoidea, 40
Plectoptera, 58
Pleospongia, 36, 42
Plesiocidaroida, 62
Plesiosauria, 67
Plesiothecata, 17, 52
Pleuracanthodii, 65
Pleurobranchomorpha, 50
Pleurocoela, 15, 50
Pleuroconcha, 50
Pleurodonta, 50
Pleurogona, 63
Pleuronectiformes, 66
Pleuronectoidea, 66
Pleuropterygii, 65
Pleuropygia, 49
Pleurosauria, 67
Pleurostigma, 57
Pleurostigmophora, 19, 57
Pleurostomata, 65
Pleurotremata, 65
Pliomeria, 54
Ploima, 13, 47
Ploimoidaceae, 47
Podicipedes, 24, 68
Podicipediformes, 24, 68
Podicipiformes, 68
Podocopa, 55
Podocopida, 18, 55
Podogonata, 18, 55
Podophthalma, 56
Poecilopoda, 54
Poecilosclerida, 10, 42
Poeobioidea, 52
Pogonofora, 59
Pogonophora, 7, 21, 37, 60
Poikilorhabdina, 41
Polyactinia, 44
Polybranchiata, 49
Polychaeta, 17, 52
Polycladida, 12, 45
Polycyclia, 44
Polycystina, 40
Polydesmoidea, 57
Polymastigina, 9, 39
Polymera, 54
Polynemiformes, 66
Polyopisthocotylea, 45

Polypiaria, 43
Polyplacophora, 49
Polyplakiphora, 49
Polyplaxiphora, 49
Polypoda, 37, 52
Polyprotodontia, 70
Polyptera, 59
Polypterei, 65
Polypteriformes, 65
Polypterini, 65
Polystomea, 45
Polythalamia, 40
Polytricha, 41
Polyzoa
    Bryozoa, 37, 48
    Platyhelminthes, 45
Porifera, 6, 10, 36, 41
Porocephalida, 17, 53
Porolepiformes, 66
Porulosida, 40
Praeheterodonta, 50
Predentata, 68
Priapulida, 14, 47
Priapuloidea, 6, 14, 36, 47
Primates, 25, 70
Prionodesmacea, 51
Proactiniae, 44
Proanura, 66
Proarthropoda, 53
Proboscidea
    Mammalia, 25, 71
    Myzostomida, 16, 51
Procellariae, 24, 68
Procellariiformes, 24, 68
Prochelicerata, 53
Procoela, 67
Procolophonia, 67
Proganosauria, 68
Progoneata, 53
Prolacertiformes, 67
Promammalia, 68, 69
Proparia, 54
Prorhipidoglossomorpha, 49
Prorocentraceae, 39
Proselachii, 65
Prosimii, 70
Prosobranchia, 15, 49
Prosopocephala, 50
Prosopora, 17, 52
Prosostomata, 45
Prosothecata, 17, 52
Prostigmata, 55
Protalcyonacea, 44
Protarthropoda, 29
Protaxonia, 27, 36
Protelytroptera, 58
Proteocephala, 12, 45
Proteocephaloidea, 45
Proteomyxa, 9, 39
Protephemerida, 57, 58
Protephemeroidea, 58

Proterandria, 57
Proterospermophora, 19, 57
Prothysanura, 57
Protichthyes, 64
Protista, 7, 26
Protoblastoidea, 60
Protoblattoidea, 58
Protobranchia, 16, 50
Protocicadida, 59
Protociliata, 10, 41
Protocoleoptera, 58
Protodiptera, 59
Protodonata, 58
Protodonta, 68
Protofulgorida, 59
Protogastropoda, 49
Protohemiptera, 58
Protohymenoptera, 58
Protomastigaceae, 39
Protomastigida, 39
Protomecoptera, 59
Protomedusae, 43
Protomonadina, 9, 39
Protonemertini, 46
Protonephridozoa, 36
Protonychophora, 53
Protoparia, 54
Protoperlaria, 58
Protorhabdina, 41
Protorosauria, 67
Protorthoptera, 58
Protospondyli, 65
Protosuchia, 67
Protosyngnatha, 57
Prototardigrada, 52
Prototheria, 25, 68, 69
Protozoa, 6, 9, 36, 39
Protracheata, 37, 52
Protremata, 15, 49
Protungulata, 70
Protura, 20, 57
Pruvostitoptera, 58
Psammosteiformes, 64
Pselaphocephala, 49
Pselaphognatha, 19, 57
Pseudanostraca, 53
Pseudaxonia, 44
Pseudechinoidea, 62
Pseudocentrophori, 66
Pseudocoelia, 36
Pseudocoelomata, 6, 36
Pseudocrustacea, 53
Pseudohemiptera, 58
Pseudolamellibranchia, 51
Pseudonotostraca, 53
Pseudophyllidea, 12, 46
Pseudorhynchota, 59
Pseudoscorpionida, 18, 54
Pseudosuchia, 67
Psittaci, 24, 69
Psittaciformes, 24, 69

Psocoptera, 20, 59
Pteraspida, 64
Pteraspides, 64
Pteraspidiformes, 64
Pteraspidomorpha, 64
Pterichthyes, 64
Pterichthyomorpha, 64
Pteriomorpha, 50
Pterobranchia, 7, 22, 37, 62
Pterocletes, 68
Pteroconchida, 50
Pterocorallia, 44
Pterodactyli, 67
Pteropoda, 16, 50
Pterosauria, 67
Pterygogenea, 57
Pterygota, 57
Ptychobranchia, 63
Ptychodactiaria, 44
Ptychopariida, 54
Ptyctodontida, 64
Ptyctodontiformes, 64
Pulicina, 59
Pulmonata, 16, 50
Pycnodontiformes, 65
Pycnodontoidea, 65
Pycnogonida, 17, 54
Pycnogonomorpha, 54
Pygaspida, 53
Pygocaulia, 49
Pygocephalomorpha, 56
Pygopodes, 68
Pyrosomata, 22, 63
Pyrosomatida, 22, 63
Pyrotheria, 71
Pythonomorpha, 67

Quadrumana, 70

Rachiglossa, 50
Radiata, 27
Radiolaria, 9, 40
Rajiformes, 65
Ralliformes, 69
Raphidioidea, 59
Ratitae, 68
Receptaculitida, 42
Reculoidea, 59
Redfieldiiformes, 65
Redlichiida, 54
Regulares, 60
Regularia
    Crinoidea, 61
    Echinoidea, 21, 62
Remigolepiformes, 64
Reptilia, 23, 67
Reptiliomorphoidea, 67
Reticularia, 40
Reticulariaceae, 40

Retioloidea, 42
Rhabdiasoidea, 14, 47
Rhabditoidea, 14, 47
Rhabdocoela, 12, 45
Rhabdogeniae, 41
Rhabdophora, 42
Rhabdopleurida, 22, 62
Rhachiglossa, 50
Rhachitomi, 66
Rheae, 24, 68
Rheiformes, 24, 68
Rhenanida, 64
Rhignogastra, 55
Rhinocarina, 56
Rhinogastra, 55
Rhipidistia, 66
Rhipidoglossa, 49
Rhipidoptera, 59
Rhipiptera, 59
Rhiptoglossa, 67
Rhizocephala, 19, 56
Rhizoflagellata, 39
Rhizomastigaceae, 39
Rhizomastigina, 9, 39
Rhizopoda, 9, 39
Rhizostomatida, 44
Rhizostomeae, 11, 44
Rhizota, 46
Rhombifera, 60
Rhomboganoidei, 65
Rhombozoa, 42
Rhynchobdellida, 17, 52
Rhynchobdelliformes, 52
Rhynchocephalia, 23, 67
Rhynchocoela, 6, 13, 36, 46
Rhynchodipteriformes, 66
Rhynchoflagellata, 39
Rhynchonellida, 48
Rhynchostomi, 54
Rhynchota, 58
Ricinuleida, 18, 55
Rodentia, 25, 70
Rophoteira, 59
Rostrata, 55
Rostroconchida, 50
Rotalidea, 40
Rotatoria, 6, 13, 36, 46
Rotifera, 6, 13, 36, 46
Roveacrinida, 60
Rugosa, 44
Rutoceratida, 51

Saccata
    Ctenophora, 45
    Mollusca, 37, 48
Saccocirrida, 52
Saccopharyngiformes, 66
Saccosomatida, 16, 51
Sacoglossa, 16, 50
Sagenocrinida, 60

Sagenocrinoidea, 60
Sagittoidea, 21, 59
Salientia, 23, 66
*Salinella,* 27
Salmopercoidea, 66
Salpida, 63
Saltatoria, 20, 58
Sarcobranchiata, 49
Sarcocystidea, 40
Sarcodina, 9, 39
Sarcosporidia, 10, 40
Saurabatrachia, 66
Sauria, 67
Saurichthyiformes, 65
Saurischia, 68
Sauropoda, 68
Sauropsida, 64
Sauropterygia, 67
Saururae, 68
Scansores, 69
Scaphopoda, 16, 50
Schistochoanites, 51
Schizocoela, 27
Schizocoralla, 44
Schizodonta, 51
Schizodontida, 50
Schizogregarinida, 41
Schizomida, 18, 55
Schizonemertini, 46
Schizonotida, 55
Schizopeltidia, 55
Schizopoda, 56
Schizosiphona, 50
Scirtopoda, 47
Scleractinia, 11, 44
Scleropareioidea, 66
Scleciformia, 52
Scolecomorpha, 49
Scolopendromorpha, 19, 57
Scopeliformes, 66
Scorpiones, 54
Scorpionida, 18, 54
Scutibranchia, 49
Scutigeromorpha, 19, 57
Scyphomedusae, 44
Scyphopolypi, 44
Scyphozoa, 11, 44
Scytactinata, 62
Scytodermata, 62
Sebecosuchia, 67
Sedentaria, 17, 52
Seisonacea, 13, 46
Seisonidea, 13, 46
Selachii, 23, 65
Selachoidea, 65
Semaeostomeae, 11, 44
Semaeostomatida, 44
Semi-articulata, 61
Semionotoidea, 65
Semostomeae, 44
Sepioidea, 51

Septibranchia, 16, 50, 51
Septibranchida, 50
Serosporidia, 41
Serpentes, 67
Sertularina, 43
Seymouriamorpha, 67
Sigmatomonaxonellida, 41
Sigmatophora, 42
Silicoflagellata, 39
Silicospongiae, 41
Simiae, 70
Simplicidentata, 70
Sinupalliata, 51
Siphonaptera, 20, 59
Siphonida, 50
Siphonobranchia, 50
Siphonophora, 11, 43
Siphonopoda, 50
Siphunculata, 59
Sipunculida, 16, 51
Sipunculoidea, 7, 16, 37, 51
Sirenia, 25, 71
Sirenoidei, 66
Solenichthyoidea, 66
Solenida, 10, 41
Solenochilida, 51
Solenoconchia, 50
Solenogastres, 15, 49
Solifugae, 18, 55
Solpugida, 18, 55
Soluta, 54
Somasteroidea, 61
Somphocyathida, 42
Sorophora, 40
Spatangoida, 22, 62
Spathebothridea, 12, 46
Spelaeogriphacea, 19, 56
Sphaeractinoidea, 43
Sphaerellaria, 40
Sphaeroidocrinacea, 60
Sphaerozoa, 40
Sphenisci, 23, 68
Sphenisciformes, 23, 68
Sphinctozoa, 41
Spinigrada, 61
Spinulosa, 21, 61
Spioniformia, 52
Spiriferida, 48
Spirigera, 41
Spirobranchia, 37, 48
Spirobranchiopoda, 48
Spironotia, 49
Spirotricha, 10, 41
Spiruroidea, 14, 48
Spongeae, 36, 41
Spongiaria, 36, 41
Spongiomorphida, 43
Sporozoa, 9, 40
Spumellaria, 40
Spyroidea, 40

Squaliformes, 65
Squaloidea, 65
Squamata
  Mammalia, 70
  Reptilia, 23, 67
Stauracea, 44
Stauromedusae, 11, 44
Steganobranchia, 50
Steganopodes, 24, 69
Stegocephalia, 66
Stegosauria, 68
Stegoselachii, 65
Stelechotokea, 44
Stelleroidea, 60
Stelliformia, 60
Stelmatopoda, 48
Stemonitaceae, 40
Stenoglossa, 50
Stenolaemata
  Bryozoa, 48
  Mollusca, 49
Stenostomata, 48
Stensiöellida, 65
Stensiöelliformes, 65
Stenurida, 61
Stephanoberyciformes, 66
Stephoidea, 40
Stereornithes, 68
Stereospondyli, 66
Stethostomata, 54
Stichodactylina, 44
Stirodonta, 62
Stolidobranchiata, 22, 63
Stolonifera, 11, 44
Stolonoidea, 43
Stomatocrinoidea, 61
Stomatopoda, 19, 56
Stomatostigmata, 55
Strepsata, 59
Strepsiptera, 21, 59
Streptoneura, 49
Streptophiurae, 61
Streptophiuroida, 61
Streptostylica, 67
Strigeata, 45
Striges, 24, 69
Strigiformes, 24, 69
Stromatoporidea, 43
Stromatoporoidea, 43
Strongyloidea, 14, 48
Strophomenida, 48
Struthiones, 23, 68
Struthioniformes, 23, 68
Stylasterina, 11, 43
Stylinodontia, 70
Stylommatophora, 16, 50
Stylopida, 59
Stylopidae, 59
Subholostei, 65
Subholosteoidea, 65
Subungulata, 70

Suctoria
  Arthropoda, 59
  Protozoa, 10, 41
Sycones, 41
Syconosa, 41
Symbranchiformes, 66
Symmetrodonta, 70
Symphyla, 19, 57
Sympoda, 56
Synalcyonacea, 44
Synapsida, 68
Synaptera, 57
Synaptida, 62
Synaptorhabda, 50
Synaptosauria, 67
Synarmogoidea, 58
Synbranchioidea, 66
Syncarida, 56
Synentognathoidea, 66
Syngnatha, 57
Syngnathiformes, 66
Syntonopteroidea, 57
Synxiphosurida, 54
Sypharopteroidea, 57
Syringocnemida, 42


Tabulata, 44
Taeniodontia, 70
Taenioglossa, 50
Taenioidea, 46
Taligrada, 70
Tanaidacea, 19, 56
Tanysitrachelia, 67
Tardigrada, 7, 17, 37, 52
Tarphyceratida, 51
Tarrasiiformes, 65
Tartarides, 55
Taxeopoda, 70
Taxocrinida, 60
Taxocrinoidea, 60
Taxodonta, 51
Taxodontia, 70
Tectibranchiata, 50
Tectobranchia, 50
Tectospondyli, 65
Teleodesmacea, 51
Teleodonta, 51
Teleoplacophora, 49
Teleostei, 23, 65
Teleostomi, 65
Telestacea, 11, 44
Telmatomorphormes, 69
Telobranchia, 49
Telogonia, 47
Telosporidia, 9, 40
Telotremata, 15, 49
Temnocephaloidea, 45
Temnospondyli, 67
Tentaculata, 12, 45

Tentaculifera
  Mollusca, 50
  Protozoa, 41
Terebelliformia, 52
Terebratulida, 48
Terricolae, 52
Tesselata, 61
Testacea
  Echinodermata, 60
  Protozoa, 9, 40
Testicardines, 49
Testudinata, 67
Testudines, 67
Tethyodeae, 63
Tetrabothridiata, 46
Tetrabranchiata, 16, 50
Tetracoelia, 44
Tetracorallia, 44
Tetracotylea, 46
Tetractinellida, 41
Tetractiniae, 45
Tetradecapoda, 56
Tetradida, 44
Tetradontiformes, 66
Tetraphyllidea, 12, 45
Tetrapoda, 64
Tetrarhyncha, 46
Tetrarhynchoidea, 46
Tetraseptata, 44
Tetraxonida, 41
Tetrodontiformes, 66
Teuthoidea, 51
Textularidea, 40
Thalamida, 10, 41
Thalamophora, 40
Thalattosauria, 67
Thalattosuchia, 67
Thaliacea, 22, 63
Thallocoralla, 44
Thecamoebae, 40
Thecanephria, 21, 60
Thecaphora, 43
Thecata, 43
Thecodontia, 67
Thecoidea, 61
Thecosomata, 50
Thelodonti, 64
Thelyphonida, 18, 55
Therapsida, 68
Theria, 69
Therictoidea, 70
Theriodontia, 68
Thermosbaenacea, 19, 56
Theromorpha, 68
Theropoda, 68
Thigmotrichina, 41
Thoracica, 18, 56
Thoracostoidea, 66
Thoracostraca, 56
Thripoides, 59
Thripsites, 59

Thrissomorphi, 66
Thunniformes, 66
Thyroidea, 61
Thyrostraca, 56
Thysanoptera, 20, 59
Thysanura, 20, 57
Tillodontia, 70
Tinami, 24, 68
Tinamiformes, 24, 68
Tintinnina, 41
Tjalfiellidea, 45
Tomiosoma, 45
Torpediniformes, 65
Toxodontia, 70
Toxoglossa, 50
Trachelosauria, 67
Trachomedusae, 43
Trachylinida, 11, 43
Trachymedusae, 43
Trachypsammiacea, 44
Tremataspidiformes, 64
Trematoda, 12, 45
Trematosauria, 66
Trepostomata, 48
Tretenterata, 49
Triaxonida, 41
Trichinelloidea, 48
Trichiaceae, 40
Trichocorallia, 44
Trichomonadida, 39
Trichoptera, 20, 59
Trichostomata, 41
Trichuroidea, 14, 48
Tricladida, 12, 45
Triconodonta, 69
Trigonotarbi, 54
Trigonotarbida, 54
Trilobita, 54
Trilobitoidea, 53
Trilobitomorpha, 52
Trimyaria, 46
Trinucleida, 54
Triplesiida, 48
Tripostomata, 48
Tripylaea, 40
Tripylaria, 40
Trituberculata, 70
Tritylodontoidea, 69
Trochelminthes, 28
Trochosphaerida, 47
Trogones, 24, 69
Trogoniformes, 24, 69
Tryblidiacea, 49
Tryblidioidea, 15, 49
Trypanorhyncha, 12, 46
Tubicola, 52
Tubinares, 24, 68
Tuboidea, 43
Tubulariae, 43
Tubulidentata, 25, 71
Tubulinaceae, 40

Tubulosa, 44
Tunicata, 7, 22, 37, 63
Turbellaria, 12, 45
Turbinares, 68

Uintacrinida, 60
Uintatheria, 71
Uncinataria, 41
Unguiculata, 70
Ungulata, 70
Ungulates, 70
Uranocyatha, 42
Urochordata, 37, 63
Urodela, 23, 66
Urodeloidei, 66
Uronemiformes, 67
Uropygi, 55

Vaginulacea, 50
Vampyromorpha, 16, 51
Veneracea, 50
Vertebrata, 7, 23, 37, 64
Volvocaceae, 39
Volvocales, 9, 39
Volvocina, 39

Waptiida, 53
Weigeltisauria, 67

Xenacanthi, 65
Xenacanthoidea, 65
Xenanthi, 65
Xenarthra, 70
Xenophyophoridea, 40
Xenopoda, 53
Xenopneusta, 16, 51
Zeomorphoidea, 66
Xiphosura, 17, 54
Xiphosurida, 17, 54

Zacanthoidacea, 54
Zeiformes, 66
Zeomorphoidea, 66
Zeuglodontia, 70
Zoa, 36
Zoantha, 44
Zoanthactiniaria, 44
Zoantharia, 11, 44
Zoanthidea, 44
Zoanthiniaria, 11, 44
Zoomastigina, 9, 39
Zoomastigophorea, 39
Zoophytaria, 44
Zoraptera, 20, 59
Zygobranchia, 49
Zygophiurae, 61